PHYSICS 12

STUDY GUIDE

SENIOR PROGRAM CONSULTANT

Maurice DiGiuseppe, Ph.D.
University of Ontario Institute of Technology (UOIT)
Formerly of Toronto Catholic District School Board

PROGRAM CONSULTANT

Charles Stewart, B.Sc., B.Ed.
Peel District School Board

NELSON EDUCATION

NELSON EDUCATION

Nelson Physics 12 Study Guide

Senior Program Consultant
Maurice DiGiuseppe

Program Consultant
Charles Stewart

Student Book Authors
Dan Bruni
Greg Dick
Jacob Speijer
Charles Stewart

Editorial Director
Linda Allison

Associate Publisher, Science
David Spiegel

Managing Editor, Science
Jennifer Hounsell

Product Manager
Doug Morrow

Program Manager
Sarah Tanzini

Project Managers
Amanda Allison
First Folio Resource Group Inc.:
Eileen Jung

Project Team
First Folio Resource Group Inc.:
Loretta Johnson
Margaret McClintock
Roland W. Meisel
Bradley T. Smith

Design Director
Ken Phipps

Interior Design
Courtney Hellam

Cover Design
Jarrel Breckon
Eugene Lo
Ken Phipps

Cover Image
*Fractal rendering of a particle
accelerator collision:* Joe White/
Shutterstock

Asset Coordinator
Suzanne Peden

Illustrators
MPS Limited
Nesbitt Graphics, Inc.
Ralph Voltz

Compositor
MPS Limited

Cover Research
Debbie Yea

Printer
Transcontinental Printing

Reviewers
The authors and publisher gratefully
acknowledge the contributions of
the following educator:
Bruce McAskill

Contents

Chapter 1: Kinematics

The slope of the position–time graph for an object gives the velocity of the object. The slope of the velocity–time graph gives the acceleration of the object. Uniformly accelerated motion can be summarized with five key equations involving displacement, initial velocity, final velocity, acceleration, and time interval.

Free fall is the motion of an object when it is moving only under the influence of gravity. The acceleration due to gravity at the surface of the Earth is 9.8 m/s^2 [down].

Displacements in two dimensions can be added using vectors. Methods of adding vectors include scale diagrams, the tip-to-tail method, and components.

Velocity and acceleration can be determined in two dimensions by using vectors to calculate changes in displacement and velocity.

A projectile is an object that moves along a trajectory through the air, with only the force of gravity acting on it. Projectile motion can be analyzed using kinematics equations for constant acceleration. Separate the motion vector into vertical and horizontal components.

Relative motion is motion observed from a specific perspective or frame of reference. Each frame of reference has its own coordinate system.

Chapter 2: Dynamics

Forces that act on everyday objects include gravity, the normal force, tension, friction, and applied force. A free-body diagram is a drawing that shows all forces on an object.

Newton's first law of motion says that an object will stay at rest or move at a constant velocity unless a net force acts on it.

Newton's second law of motion says that the net force acting on an object equals its mass multiplied by its acceleration.

Newton's third law of motion says that when body A exerts a force on body B, body B exerts an equal and opposite force on body A. The weight of an object is the force of gravity acting on it. If the net force acting on an object is zero, it is in equilibrium. The frictional force between two bodies equals the coefficient of friction multiplied by the normal force pushing them together.

Chapter 3: Uniform Circular Motion

A frame of reference is a choice of coordinate system for making measurements. An inertial frame of reference is at rest or moves at a constant velocity. A non-inertial frame of reference is accelerating. Fictitious forces appear in non-inertial frames of reference.

A body that follows a circular path at constant speed has a centripetal acceleration directed toward the centre of the circular path. A body requires a centripetal force to move in a circular path.

Centrifugal force is a fictitious force that appears to affect bodies measured in a rotating frame of reference.

The Coriolis force is a fictitious force that acts perpendicular to the velocity of a body in a rotating frame of reference.

BIG IDEAS

- Forces affect motion in predictable and quantifiable ways.
- Forces acting on an object will determine the motion of that object.
- Many technologies that utilize the principles of dynamics have societal and environmental implications.

Motion and Motion Graphs

Textbook pp. 8–16

Vocabulary

kinematics	displacement ($\Delta \vec{d}$)	tangent
dynamics	average speed (v_{av})	instantaneous velocity ($\vec{v}$)
scalar	velocity ($\vec{v}$)	instantaneous speed (v)
vector	average velocity ($\vec{v}_{av}$)	average acceleration ($\vec{a}_{av}$)
position ($\vec{d}$)	secant	instantaneous acceleration ($\vec{a}$)

MAIN IDEA: The equation for average speed is $v_{av} = \dfrac{\Delta d}{\Delta t}$, and the equation for average velocity is $\vec{v}_{av} = \dfrac{\Delta \vec{d}}{\Delta t}$.

1. Examine **Figure 1** and **Figure 2**. One of the graphs shown represents speed versus time for an object, while the other represents acceleration versus time for the same object. Which is which? Explain. K/U C

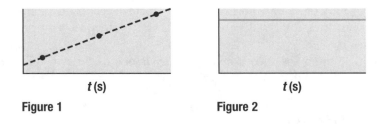

Figure 1   **Figure 2**

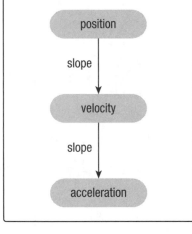
2. A light aircraft flies 120 km [E] in 0.80 h, then 40 km [W] in 0.20 h. K/U T/I A
   (a) Calculate the average speed of the aircraft for the easterly portion of the flight.

   (b) Calculate the average velocity of the aircraft for the easterly portion of the flight.

(c) Calculate the average speed of the aircraft for the total flight.

(d) Calculate the average velocity of the aircraft for the total flight.

(e) Is it possible for the aircraft to fly one more leg that results in an average speed that is not zero, but an average velocity equal to zero? If not, explain why. If so, determine the speed and direction for the additional leg.

MAIN IDEA: The slope of the position–time graph for a moving object gives the velocity of the object.

3. An object moves according to the position–time graph shown in **Figure 3**. T/I A

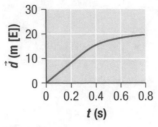

Figure 3

(a) Determine the average velocity of the object from $t_1 = 0$ s to $t_2 = 0.8$ s.

(b) Determine the instantaneous velocity at $t = 0.4$ s.

MAIN IDEA: Acceleration describes how quickly an object's velocity changes over time.

The equation for average acceleration is $\vec{a}_{av} = \dfrac{\Delta \vec{v}}{\Delta t}$. The slope of the velocity–time graph gives the object's acceleration.

4. **Figure 4** shows the velocity–time graph for a cyclist.

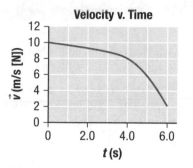

Figure 4

(a) Determine the average acceleration of the cyclist from $t = 0.0$ s to $t = 6.0$ s.

(b) Determine the instantaneous acceleration at $t = 5.0$ s.

1.1 Motion and Motion Graphs   **5**

Equations of Motion

Textbook pp. 17–21

Vocabulary

free fall

MAIN IDEA: The five key equations for uniformly accelerated motion involve the variables: displacement, initial velocity, final velocity, acceleration, and time interval.

1. **Figure 1** shows the velocity–time graph for a motorcyclist heading north. Explain how you can determine the displacement of the motorcyclist from the velocity–time graph. Provide several methods. Use one method to determine the displacement. K/U T/I A

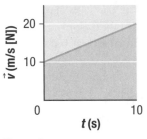

Figure 1

2. An oil tanker sailing west has an engine problem. It coasts to a stop in 0.50 h, moving 10 km in a straight line. What is the average acceleration of the ship? T/I A

3. While driving on a slippery road at 15.0 m/s [E], the driver applies the brakes to come to a stop. The braking system limits the acceleration to 0.200 m/s² [W] or causes a deceleration of −0.200 m/s² [W]. Determine the stopping distance for the car. T/I A

4. A toy car at the 0 cm mark on a metre stick moves toward the 100 cm mark at a constant speed of 5.0 cm/s. Another toy car starts at the 100 cm mark at the same time, accelerating toward the 0 cm mark at 1.0 m/s^2. How long will it take for the two cars to collide? K/U T/I

MAIN IDEA: Free fall is the motion of an object when it is moving only under the influence of gravity. The acceleration due to gravity at the surface of the Earth is 9.8 m/s^2 [down].

5. A ball launcher on the ground is aimed straight up, and it launches a baseball with an initial velocity of 49.0 m/s [up]. The ball continues upward to a stop, and then falls until caught by a player leaning out of a window 78.4 m above the ground. How long is the ball in the air before the player catches it? K/U T/I

6. While flying her helicopter in a hovering position 40.0 m above the ground, the pilot threw a rope with an initial velocity of 4.00 m/s [down]. What is the speed of the rope at the instant that it hits the ground? K/U T/I

Displacement in Two Dimensions

Vocabulary

component of a vector

MAIN IDEA: To add displacement vectors, draw a scale diagram with the vectors tip to tail on graph paper. Measure the length of the total displacement vector, and rescale to the desired units. Instead of an accurate scale diagram, you can use a sketch, and then apply the sine law or cosine law as appropriate.

1. Sunita started at City Hall, walked 3.0 km [N], then another 4.0 km [N]. Franz walked with Sunita for the first leg of the trip, then turned and walked 4.0 km [W]. Which statement is true? Provide support for your answer. **K/U**

    (a) Both experienced the same total displacement.

    (b) Franz walked farther than Sunita.

    (c) Sunita's displacement had a magnitude larger than Franz's displacement.

    (d) Franz's displacement had a magnitude larger than Sunita's displacement.

2. Is the following statement true or false? If you think the statement is false, rewrite it to make it true: The magnitude of the total displacement is always less than or equal to the total distance travelled. **K/U**

3. Tomas flew his airplane 80 km [W 30° N]. He then turned directly north, and flew an additional 60 km. **K/U** **T/I** **C**

    (a) Use a scale diagram to determine the total displacement.

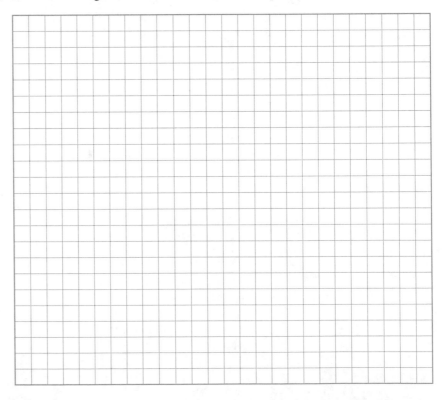

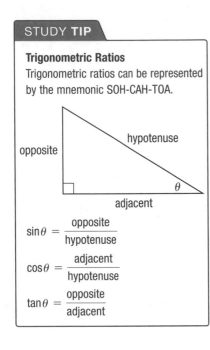

(b) Use the sine law and/or cosine law to determine the total displacement.

(c) Compare your answers from parts (a) and (b). Comment on the accuracy of each method used.

MAIN IDEA: Two-dimensional displacement vectors can be resolved into two perpendicular component vectors, one parallel to the x-axis and one parallel to the y-axis. Use the sine and cosine ratios to determine these perpendicular components. Add the x-components to determine the x-component of the total displacement vector. Add the y-components to determine the y-component of the total displacement vector. Use these components of the total displacement vector to determine the total displacement vector $\Delta \vec{d}_T$.

4. A boat left harbour and proceeded 20 km 37° south of east. Without making calculations, which of these could be the correct components of the displacement vector? Explain your reasoning. K/U T/I

   (a) $\Delta d_x = 16$ km $[E]$; $\Delta d_y = 12$ km $[S]$ (c) $\Delta d_x = 16$ km $[S]$; $\Delta d_y = 12$ km $[E]$
   (b) $\Delta d_x = 12$ km $[E]$; $\Delta d_y = 16$ km $[S]$ (d) $\Delta d_x = 12$ km $[S]$; $\Delta d_y = 16$ km $[E]$

5. Halmi rode his bicycle 5.0 km in a direction 30° north of east, and then an additional 9.0 km in a direction 45° south of east. Use algebraic addition of vector components to determine Halmi's total displacement. K/U T/I

6. Kristen skateboarded 15.5 km in a direction 37° north of west, and then an additional 15.0 km in a direction 64° south of west. Use algebraic addition of vector components to determine Kristen's total displacement. K/U T/I C

Velocity and Acceleration in Two Dimensions

Textbook pp. 30–35

MAIN IDEA: Average velocity in two dimensions is the total displacement in two dimensions divided by the time interval in which the displacement occurs: $\vec{v}_{av} = \dfrac{\Delta \vec{d}}{\Delta t}$.

STUDY TIP

Using Geometry Software
You can check your solutions to vector problems using dynamic geometry software.

---

1. A scuba diver swims 60 m [E] to a coral outcrop, and then 80 m [N] to a sunken anchor. The total time for the trip is 200 s. Make only one simple calculation, and decide which of these could be the average velocity for the trip. Explain your reasoning. K/U T/I

   (a) 140 m/s [E 53° N]
   (b) 0.70 m/s [E 53° N]
   (c) 0.50 m/s [E 37° N]
   (d) 0.50 m/s [E 53° N]

2. A hiker used a compass to orient himself as he walked 3.00 km in a direction 50.0° north of west, and then an additional 2.00 km in a direction 20.0° south of west. The trip took 1.00 h. Determine the average velocity of the hiker. K/U T/I

MAIN IDEA: You can determine the change in velocity in two dimensions ($\Delta \vec{v}$) by separating the velocity vectors into components and subtracting the corresponding components. Alternatively, you can perform vector subtraction using the vector property $\vec{v_f} - \vec{v_i} = \vec{v_f} + (-\vec{v_i})$ and following the procedure for vector addition.

3. Vector $\vec{A}$ has a length of 10 units and points [north]. Vector $\vec{B}$ has a length of 24 units and points [east]. Without drawing a diagram, determine the direction of vector $\vec{A} - \vec{B}$. Explain your reasoning. K/U T/I C

   (a) southwest
   (b) southeast
   (c) northwest
   (d) northeast

4. Sally rode her motorcycle [E 40° S] at 60.0 km/h. She then turned to a direction of [E 25° N] and increased her speed to 80.0 km/h. Determine her change in velocity. K/U T/I

MAIN IDEA: Average acceleration in two dimensions is the change in velocity divided by the time interval between the two velocities: $\vec{a}_{av} = \dfrac{\Delta \vec{v}}{\Delta t} = \dfrac{\vec{v_f} - \vec{v_i}}{\Delta t}$

5. Is the following statement true or false? If you think the statement is false, rewrite it to make it true: A car heading north at 100 km/h is subjected to a constant acceleration directed to the east. No matter how long the acceleration persists, the velocity vector of the car will always point between north and east, never reaching east. K/U T/I

6. A motorboat was moving [E 20° S] at 50.0 km/h. The operator then turned the boat [E 20° N] and decreased the speed to 30.0 km/h over 5.0 min. Determine the average acceleration of the boat. K/U T/I

Projectile Motion

Textbook pp. 36–43

Vocabulary

projectile   range (Δd_x)   projectile motion

MAIN IDEA: A projectile is an object that moves along a trajectory with only the force of gravity acting on it. An object moving with projectile motion has a constant horizontal velocity and a constant vertical acceleration.

Kinematic Equations with Horizontal and Vertical Components

STUDY TIP

Table of Equations
This is an excellent place to make use of your Equation Organizer. You can use the opportunity to fine tune how you have the equations organized, and add notes on where they apply.

Direction of motion	Description	Equations of motion
horizontal motion (x)	constant-velocity equation for the x-component only	$v_{ix} = v_i \cos \theta$ $v_{ix} = \text{constant}$ $\Delta d_x = v_{ix} \Delta t$ $\Delta d_x = (v_i \cos \theta)\Delta t$
vertical motion (y)	constant-acceleration equations for the y-component; constant acceleration has a magnitude of $|\vec{g}| = g = 9.8 \text{ m/s}^2$	$v_{fy} = v_i \sin \theta - g\Delta t$ $\Delta d_y = (v_i \sin \theta)\Delta t - \frac{1}{2}g\Delta t^2$ $v_{fy}^2 = (v_i \sin \theta)^2 - 2g\Delta d_y$

1. A red ball is launched horizontally at a speed of 5.0 m/s. A green ball is dropped at the same time from the same point. If both balls land on the same level floor, which statement is true? Explain your answer. **K/U** **T/I** **C**
   (a) The red ball will hit the floor before the green ball.
   (b) The green ball will hit the floor before the red ball.
   (c) Both balls will hit the floor at the same time.
   (d) There is not enough information to make the determination.

2. A golfer hits a ball, and it lands at the same vertical level it was launched. The launch angle can be increased from 0° to 90°. Which statement is true? Explain why your choice is correct, and the other choices are not correct. **K/U** **T/I** **C** **A**
   (a) The time the ball spent in the air is the same for all launch angles.
   (b) The range will increase as the launch angle is increased from 0° to 90°.
   (c) The maximum height reached is the same for all launch angles.
   (d) The time spent in the air increases as the launch angle is increased from 0° to 90°.

MAIN IDEA: The horizontal and vertical motions of a projectile are independent. The time that a projectile spends moving in the horizontal direction is the same time that it moves in the vertical direction.

3. An archer released an arrow at a speed of 80.0 m/s at an angle of 40° above the horizontal. 1.63 s later, the arrow struck the target at the same height above ground as the launch point. How far was the target from the archer? **T/I** **A**

4. A punter kicks a football at an angle of 30.0° above the horizontal. The football lands 86.9 m from the point it was kicked 3.20 s later. K/U T/I A

(a) What is the launch speed of the football?

(b) What is the maximum height reached by the football?

MAIN IDEA: To solve projectile motion problems, apply the constant-velocity equation for the horizontal displacement, and apply the constant-acceleration equations for the vertical motion.

5. A catapult constructed by a student can launch a bowling ball at a speed of 19.6 m/s. What is the expected maximum range of the catapult, assuming that the ball lands at the same height from which it is launched? Explain your reasoning. K/U T/I C A

6. A pumpkin farm holds an annual pumpkin launch. Visitors may guess the distance a launched pumpkin will travel. The farm's catapult launches the pumpkin at a speed of 25.2 m/s. Assume that the pumpkin will land at the same height from which it is launched. George guesses a range of 60.0 m. Christy guesses a range of 65.0 m. Who guessed correctly? Explain your answer. K/U T/I

7. Andrew is standing 10.0 m from Juliet's house. Andrew tosses a ball to Juliet, and the ball travels at 5.00 m/s at an angle of 50.0° above the ground. The ball passes through Juliet's window. How far above the ground is the window? K/U T/I

$\Delta d_x = 10.0$ m
$V_i = 5.00 \frac{m}{s}$
$\theta = 50.0°$

$\sin 50 = \frac{V_{ix}}{V_i}$
$V_{ix} = 3.83$

$\cos 50 = \frac{V_{iy}}{V_i}$
$V_{iy} = 3.21$

$V_x = \frac{\Delta d_x}{\Delta t}$
$\Delta t = 2.61$

Relative Motion

Textbook pp. 44–49

> **Vocabulary**
>
> frame of reference   relative velocity

MAIN IDEA: Relative motion is motion observed from a specific perspective or frame of reference. Each frame of reference has its own coordinate system.

1. Albert is driving his car at 100 km/h, and Beata is driving her car at 95 km/h on the same road. If they collide, would a head-on collision cause more damage than a rear-end collision? Explain your answer using numbers to support your statements. K/U C

2. Sandor is in the basket of a hot-air balloon that is drifting west with a wind of 20 km/h. He takes out a Canadian flag and holds it up. Which statement is correct? Explain your answer. K/U C
   (a) The flag will flutter towards the east.
   (b) The flag will flutter towards the west.
   (c) The flag will droop as if there is no wind.
   (d) There is not enough information to determine a correct answer.

MAIN IDEA: Relative velocity is the velocity of an object observed from a specific frame of reference. The relative velocity equation is $\vec{v}_{AC} = \vec{v}_{AB} + \vec{v}_{BC}$ where A is the object moving relative to the frame of reference C, which is moving relative to the frame of reference B.

3. A plane is flying, moving relative to the air at 385.0 km/h [S], but the air velocity relative to Earth is 56.0 km/h [N]. What is the velocity of the plane relative to Earth? K/U T/I A

> **STUDY TIP**
>
> **Drawing Diagrams**
> Use diagrams to give you a picture of the problem. Label the diagram with as much of the given information as possible.

4. Randall paddles his canoe at 2.0 m/s in still water. He drops the canoe into a river which is flowing north at 1.5 m/s. T/I A

(a) If he paddles north, what is the velocity of the canoe relative to Earth?

(b) If he paddles south, what is the velocity of the canoe relative to Earth?

(c) If he paddles east, what is the velocity of the canoe relative to Earth?

5. Lindsay is planning a flight from St. Catharines to Hamilton, which lies due west of St. Catharines. Her aircraft flies at a speed of 200 km/h in still air. A wind of 50.0 km/h is blowing from [W 60° N]. In what direction must she aim the airplane to fly directly to Hamilton? T/I A

6. A helicopter is flying from Belleville to Kingston, which lies due east of Belleville. The helicopter flies at a speed of 160.0 km/h in still air. A wind of 45.0 km/h is blowing from [E 56° N]. In what direction must the pilot aim the helicopter to fly directly to Kingston? T/I A

Kinematics

Use the graphic organizer below to summarize what you have learned about kinematics. Add arrows to show the connections between concepts. You can add your own notes, diagrams, and equations to this graphic organizer, creating a study tool to help you review Chapter 1.

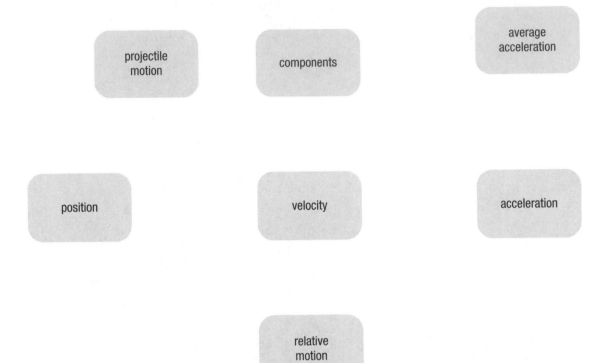

1. The position–time graph for an object is a horizontal straight line. What conclusion(s) can be drawn? (1.1) **K/U**
   (a) The velocity of the object is zero.
   (b) The velocity of the object is either zero or has a constant magnitude.
   (c) The position of the object is zero.
   (d) Both (a) and (c) are true.

2. The average velocity of an object over a time interval Δt is zero. What conclusion is always true in this case? (1.4) **K/U**
   (a) The object does not move from its starting position during Δt.
   (b) The starting position and the final position are the same.
   (c) The acceleration of the object during Δt is zero.
   (d) The speed of the object is always zero during Δt.

3. Indicate whether each statement is true or false. If you think a statement is false, rewrite it to make it true. **K/U**
   (a) An object moved 10 cm and then 12 cm in the opposite direction, so the total distance travelled is 22 cm. (1.3)

   (b) A car is being driven around a circular track at a speed of 120 km/h, so its velocity is constant. (1.4)

   (c) Projectile motion occurs when horizontal acceleration is zero and vertical acceleration is only due to gravity. (1.5)

   (d) A frame of reference is a coordinate system relative to which motion is observed. (1.6)

4. Refer to **Figure 1**. Determine the instantaneous velocity at $t = 0.40$ s. (1.1) **T/I** **C**

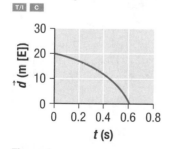

Figure 1

K/U Knowledge/Understanding
T/I Thinking/Investigation
C Communication
A Application

5. An airliner lands on runway 18, which points south. The pilot applies reverse thrust, and brings the plane to a stop in 20.0 s, moving 1.20 km in a straight line. What is the average acceleration of the airliner? (1.2) T/I A

6. During the swimming event at a triathlon, a swimmer swam 4.00 km in a direction 50° north of east, and then an additional 6.00 km in a direction 40° south of east. Use algebraic addition of vector components to determine the total displacement vector. (1.3) T/I A

7. An aerobatic pilot is flying his airplane at 250 km/h horizontally west when he pulls it into a vertical climb [N]. After 3.0 s the airplane is flying straight up at 150 km/h. Determine the average acceleration of the airplane. (1.4) T/I A

8. Design a physics problem that you would solve using the projectile motion equations. Provide a full worked solution to your problem. (1.5) T/I C A

9. Deepa has a boat with a motor that drives it at 4.5 km/h in still water. She starts motoring downstream in a river at 9:00 a.m. The current in the river moves at 2.5 km/h. At 9:30 a.m., one of the lifejackets fell overboard and started drifting downstream on its own. At 10:00 a.m., Deepa noticed the missing lifejacket. She turned the boat and motored upstream. At what time did she recover the lifejacket? Explain your reasoning. (1.6) T/I A

Forces and Free-Body Diagrams

Vocabulary

force ($\vec{F}$)	normal force ($\vec{F}_N$)	air resistance ($\vec{F}_{air}$)
newton	tension ($\vec{F}_T$)	applied force ($\vec{F}_a$)
contact force	friction ($\vec{F}_f$)	free-body diagram
non-contact force	static friction ($\vec{F}_s$)	net force ($\Sigma\vec{F}$)
force of gravity ($\vec{F}_g$)	kinetic friction ($\vec{F}_K$)	

Textbook pp. 60–69

MAIN IDEA: Examples of forces that you encounter every day are Earth's gravity, the normal force, tension, friction, applied forces, and air resistance. Static friction prevents a stationary object from moving, and kinetic friction opposes the motion of an object. Air resistance opposes the motion of an object through the air.

1. A skater moving west along an ice surface falls and slides to a stop. Which force is responsible for slowing the skater? Explain why the other choices are not correct. K/U T/I

   (a) gravity
   (b) kinetic friction

   (c) the normal force
   (d) all of these

> **STUDY TIP**
>
> **Use a Graphic Organizer**
> Be sure to add equations in this chapter to your equation sheet. Use a graphic organizer to group equations by topic. One group may be Kinematics, another Dynamics, etc.

2. Is the following statement true or false? If you think the statement is false, rewrite it to make it true: A skydiver opens her parachute and falls at a constant speed; at this time, the only force acting on the skydiver–parachute combination is gravity. K/U T/I

3. A glider is towed aloft by a cable pulled by a powered airplane. Indicate all of the forces listed that act on the glider during the tow. Justify each selection. K/U T/I

   ☐ applied force
   ☐ air resistance

   ☐ gravity
   ☐ static friction

   ☐ kinetic friction
   ☐ tension

MAIN IDEA: A free-body diagram (FBD) is a simple drawing of an object that shows all forces acting on the object. FBDs can help you visualize the forces, determine the components, and calculate the net force. The net force, $\Sigma\vec{F}$, is the sum of all of the forces acting on an object.

4. A tourist in Costa Rica takes a zip line tour through the forest canopy. The line slopes downward to the west making an angle of 10° with the horizontal. T/I C A

   (a) Sketch a simple system diagram.   (b) Draw an FBD.

5. The chandelier in a theatre production weighs 500.0 N. During the first act, it is pulled out of the view of the audience toward the west with a horizontal rope, such that its supporting rope makes an angle of 20° with the vertical.

K/U T/I A

(a) Sketch a simple system diagram.   (b) Draw an FBD.

(c) Determine the tension in the horizontal rope.

Newton's Laws of Motion

Vocabulary		
inertia	mass	weight

Textbook pp. 70–76

MAIN IDEA: Newton's first law of motion states that when the external net force on an object is zero, the object will remain at rest or continue moving at a constant velocity. Inertia is the property of matter that causes matter to resist changes in motion. An object's inertia is directly proportional to the mass of the object.

1. Juan is given the following problem: A car is moving south at 80 km/h. The engine of the car runs out of fuel and the car coasts to a stop. Juan predicts the car will stop because a net force is needed to maintain a constant velocity. Is he correct? Explain. K/U T/I A

2. Bertrande was riding her bicycle down the road with a velocity of 5.0 m/s [W]. She struck a parked car. Later she said, "The bicycle stopped, but I was thrown over the handlebars into the car." Is she correct? Explain your answer. K/U

3. A car moving at 50 km/h can be stopped in a few metres. An oil tanker moving at 50 km/h requires several kilometres to come to a stop. Explain why this is true. K/U

MAIN IDEA: Newton's second law of motion states that when the net external force on an object is not zero, the object will accelerate in the direction of the net force. The magnitude of the acceleration is directly proportional to the magnitude of the net force and inversely proportional to the mass:

$$\vec{a} = \frac{\Sigma \vec{F}}{m} \text{ or } \Sigma \vec{F} = m\vec{a}$$

4. The engine and propeller of an airplane exert a forward force of 400.0 N on the airplane. Air resistance exerts a backward force of 250 N. The mass of the airplane and payload totals 1500 kg. Determine the acceleration of the airplane. T/I A

5. Two Arctic explorers are pulling a supply sled with a total mass of 160 kg. Alphonse pulls the sled with a force of 50.0 N [E 25° N], while Bela pulls the sled with a force of 80.0 N [E 20° S]. Determine the acceleration of the sled. T/I A

MAIN IDEA: Newton's third law of motion states that for every action force, there exists a simultaneous reaction force that is equal in magnitude, but opposite in direction.

6. Balint says, "Newton's third law must be wrong. It states that forces always occur in equal and opposite pairs. These forces should always cancel each other, and nothing should ever experience a net force. Therefore, nothing should ever change its motion." Is he correct? Support your argument with an example. K/U

7. A skydiver jumps from an aircraft and falls freely. Earth exerts a downward force on the skydiver. According to Newton's third law,
   (a) the skydiver exerts an equal and upward force on Earth
   (b) gravity exerts an equal and downward force on the skydiver
   (c) the air exerts an equal and upward force on the skydiver
   (d) the air exerts an equal and downward force on the skydiver K/U

MAIN IDEA: Earth's force of gravity on an object is the object's weight. The acceleration due to Earth's gravity is 9.8 m/s² downward. The force of gravity at Earth's surface is determined using the equation $\vec{F} = m\vec{g}$.

8. Sitara has a mass of 60.0 kg. What is her weight on Earth? K/U A

Applying Newton's Laws of Motion

Vocabulary	
equilibrium	Textbook pp. 77–83

MAIN IDEA: An object is in equilibrium when the net force on it is zero. If an object is not in equilibrium, then it is accelerating in some direction.

1. Which of the following bodies are in equilibrium? Explain your answer. K/U T/I
   (a) A chandelier hanging at rest from the ceiling.
   (b) A helicopter flying north at a constant speed and altitude.
   (c) A skydiver falling at terminal velocity.
   (d) All of the above.

> **LEARNING TIP**
>
> **Moving Bodies and Equilibrium**
> A common error is to assume that, if a body is moving, it cannot be in equilibrium. If the body has a constant velocity, then it is not accelerating. Therefore, the net force acting on it is zero, and it is in equilibrium.

2. A scuba diver with a total mass of 80.0 kg experiences a buoyant force in the water of 900.0 N [up]. How much extra weight, in terms of force, must she add to her weight belt to achieve equilibrium? T/I A

3. A 75 kg rock climber is attached to a rope that is allowing her to hang horizontally with her feet against the wall. The tension in the rope is 825 N and the rope makes an angle of 35° with the vertical. Determine the force exerted by the wall on the climber's feet. T/I A

MAIN IDEA: Problems involving forces can generally be solved using a common strategy based on Newton's laws. FBDs are helpful for solving problems involving force. For objects experiencing forces in two dimensions, break the motion into perpendicular components which can be analyzed independently. Once you have determined the net force using components, use Newton's second law to determine the acceleration.

4. A bird with a mass of 1.20 kg sits in the middle of a stretched telephone wire, such that each half of the wire makes an angle of 10.0° with the horizontal.

   T/I C

   (a) Sketch an FBD of the situation.

   (b) Determine the magnitude of the tension in the wire.

5. Yua attached a kite with a mass of 325 g to a string and flew it in a strong easterly wind. The string made an angle of 60.0° with the horizontal and exerted a force of 2.75 N on the kite. The kite accelerated upward at 1.20 m/s². Determine the force exerted by the wind on the kite. K/U T/I

Forces of Friction

Textbook pp. 84–90

Vocabulary

coefficient of kinetic friction (μ_K) coefficient of static friction (μ_S)

MAIN IDEA: The coefficients of kinetic friction and static friction relate the force of friction between two objects to the normal force acting at the surfaces of the objects. These coefficients have no units and depend on the nature of the surfaces. The frictional force increases as the normal force increases. The force of kinetic friction $F_K = \mu_K F_N$ always opposes motion.

1. The driver of a car moving at 50 km/h applies the brakes, and brings the car to a stop without skidding. What is the force that stops the car? Explain your answer. [K/U] [C]

   (a) The force of the driver's foot pushing on the brake pedal.

   (b) The force of static friction between the tires and the ground.

   (c) The force of kinetic friction between the tires and the ground.

   (d) The normal force between the tires and the ground.

2. A baseball player with a mass of 65.0 kg is sliding forward into home plate. The coefficient of friction between the player and the ground is 0.124. What is the force of kinetic friction acting on the player? [T/I] [A]

MAIN IDEA: The force of static friction $F_S = \mu_S F_N$ opposes the force applied to an object. The force of static friction increases as the applied force increases, until the maximum static friction is reached. At that instant, the object begins to move and kinetic friction opposes the motion. The coefficient of kinetic friction is less than or equal to the coefficient of static friction.

3. After suffering an engine failure in his small airplane, a pilot brings the aircraft into a level but short field for an emergency landing. Once the wheels are firmly on the ground, what is the best action to take? Explain your answer. [K/U] [A]

   (a) Apply the brakes as gently as possible.

   (b) Apply the brakes in an effort to lock the wheels into a skid.

   (c) Apply left brake, then right brake, alternating between the two.

   (d) Apply the brakes as strongly as possible without going into a skid.

> **LEARNING TIP**
>
> **Errors with Static Friction**
> A common error is to assume that, given two bodies, the force of static friction between them is constant. If a box is placed on the floor, at rest, the static friction is zero. If someone exerts a horizontal force on the box, but the box does not move, the static friction is equal in magnitude to the applied force.

4. A mass, m_1, of 250 g is on a table connected to mass m_2 with a massless string over a frictionless pulley, as shown in **Figure 1**. The coefficient of friction between m_1 and the table is 0.228. What is the maximum value of m_2 before m_1 starts sliding across the table? T/I A

Figure 1

5. A box with a mass of 10.0 kg is placed on a hill that inclines upward at an angle of 30.0°. The coefficient of static friction between the box and the hill is 0.582, while the coefficient of kinetic friction is 0.528. If the box is given an initial push to start it moving down the hill, will it continue moving down the hill when the initial force is removed, or will it coast to a stop? Explain your reasoning. T/I A

Linear Actuators

Textbook pp. 91–92

> **Vocabulary**
>
> linear actuator

MAIN IDEA: A linear actuator converts energy into motion to turn a gear, which turns a screw, which pushes on a plunger that applies a linear constant force.

1. Ergonomics is the study of
   (a) the health levels in a working environment
   (b) the safety of workers in a working environment
   (c) the design and efficiency of different working environments
   (d) all of the above [K/U]

2. Linear actuators are desirable in a working environment because they
   (a) can prevent muscle, joint, or nerve injuries
   (b) can apply a uniform force
   (c) are inexpensive
   (d) all of the above [K/U]

3. Indicate whether each statement is true or false. If you think the statement is false, rewrite it to make it true. [K/U]
   (a) The stroke of a linear actuator refers to the speed at which the plunger can move.

   (b) A pneumatic linear actuator uses the potential energy in a compressed liquid.

4. Use a graphic organizer to compare the advantages and disadvantages of a mechanical linear actuator to a pneumatic linear actuator. Consider cost, power source, reliability, and precision. [T/I] [C]

> **LEARNING TIP**
>
> **Use Videos**
> You can view video clips of various linear actuators in action on the Internet. Search using the keywords "linear actuator."

— *Physics* JOURNAL —

Textbook pp. 93–94

The Physics of Downhill Skiing

MAIN IDEA: Downhill skiing involves forces such as gravity, air resistance, and kinetic friction. The skier can use stance and equipment to reduce air resistance and kinetic friction to help reach the bottom of the slope more quickly, and use friction to help maintain control.

1. Complete the statement then explain your choice. K/U

   A skier adds wax to the bottom of the skis to

   (a) reduce the kinetic friction between the skis and the snow to increase acceleration.

   (b) increase the kinetic friction between the skis and the snow in order to improve control.

   (c) reduce air resistance.

   (d) melt the snow directly under the skis.

2. Indicate whether the following statement is true or false. If you think the statement is false, rewrite it to make it true. A skier with greater mass will accelerate due to gravity faster than a skier with a smaller mass. K/U

3. Which statement best describes air resistance? K/U

   (a) It does not affect the speed of a skier.

   (b) It can be reduced by adopting a crouching position.

   (c) It has a smaller effect on more massive skiers.

   (d) It acts opposite to kinetic friction when skiing.

4. Which statement about skiing turns is true? K/U

   (a) A lighter skier can usually make turns of smaller radius.

   (b) Turns of smaller radius decrease the time required to reach the bottom of the slope.

   (c) Side cuts reduce the radius of a turn.

   (d) all of the above

5. A student sketches an FBD for a skier sliding down a hill (**Figure 1**). What change should be made to the FBD? Explain your reasoning. K/U C A

   (a) The direction of the air resistance vector should be reversed.

   (b) The direction of the kinetic friction vector should be reversed.

   (c) The net force vector should be added.

   (d) The FBD is correct as it stands.

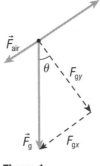

Figure 1

Dynamics

You have learned about Newton's three laws of motion and dynamics. Use the graphic organizer below to summarize what you have learned about dynamics. Add arrows to show connections. You can add your own notes, diagrams, and equations to this graphic organizer, creating a study tool to help you review Chapter 2.

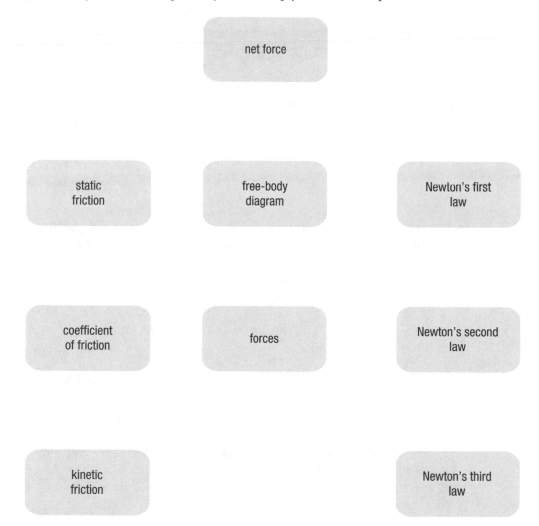

net force

static friction

free-body diagram

Newton's first law

coefficient of friction

forces

Newton's second law

kinetic friction

Newton's third law

K/U Knowledge/Understanding
T/I Thinking/Investigation
C   Communication
A   Application

1. A book with a weight of 10.0 N is on a desk. The coefficient of static friction between the book and the desk is 0.500. A student pushes the book sideways with a force of 4.00 N. The book does not move. What is the force of static friction opposing the motion of the book? (2.1, 2.3, 2.4) K/U
   (a) 6.00 N   (c) 4.00 N
   (b) 5.00 N   (d) 0 N

2. A hose is immersed in a swimming pool. The water is turned on, and the hose snakes back and forth in the pool. This is a demonstration of
   (a) Newton's first law of motion   (c) Newton's third law of motion
   (b) Newton's second law of motion   (d) inertia (2.2) K/U A

3. Indicate whether each statement is true or false. If you think the statement is false, rewrite it to make it true. K/U
   (a) An object is in equilibrium if its instantaneous velocity at some point is zero. (2.3)

   (b) A sled is placed on a snow-covered hill, but does not slide down the hill. The force of kinetic friction between the sled and the snow must be equal to the component of its weight acting down the hill. (2.4)

   (c) A linear actuator uses energy to apply a constant force. (2.5)

   (d) The force of kinetic friction between a skier and the snow depends on the mass of the skier. (2.6)

4. A gardener pushes a lawnmower with a mass of 15.0 kg toward the east with a force of 30.0 N directed down the handle. The handle makes an angle of 60.0° with the horizontal. Assume that the friction between the wheels and the ground is negligible. (2.1) T/I C A
   (a) Draw an FBD.
   (b) Determine the net force on the lawnmower.

5. A canoe and a paddler have a combined mass of 100.0 kg. The canoe is dropped into a river flowing from east to west. The flowing water exerts a force of 18.0 N on the canoe. The paddler exerts a force of 36.0 N [E 37.0° N]. Determine the net force on the canoe at this instant. (2.2) T/I A

6. Jolienne is parasailing at the end of a rope attached to a motorboat moving south. Jolienne and the sail have a mass of 75.0 kg, and are moving with a constant velocity. The rope exerts a force of 100.0 N and makes an angle of 35.0° with the horizontal. Determine the force of the wind on the sail. (2.3) T/I A

7. A ski-plane with a total mass of 1200 kg lands toward the west on a frozen lake at 30.0 m/s. The coefficient of kinetic friction between the skis and the ice is 0.200. How far does the plane slide before coming to a stop? (2.4) T/I A

8. Design a physics problem involving a body in equilibrium and at least three forces. Provide a full worked solution to your problem. (2.2, 2.3, 2.4) T/I C A

9. Use Newton's laws of motion to explain how a skier jumping from a plane can be injured when he strikes the ground below. Suggest at least two safety devices he could wear to lessen the chance of serious injury and describe how they work. (2.6) T/I C A

Inertial and Non-inertial Frames of Reference

Vocabulary

frame of reference

inertial frame of reference

non-inertial frame of reference

fictitious force

apparent weight

MAIN IDEA: A frame of reference is a choice of coordinate system, including an origin, that is used for making measurements. An inertial frame of reference is one that moves at a constant velocity or is at rest. The law of inertia holds. A non-inertial frame of reference is one that undergoes acceleration because of some external force. The law of inertia does not hold.

1. Classify each of these frames of reference as inertial or non-inertial. K/U

   (a) A car moving in a straight line at 50 km/h. _____

   (b) An airplane climbing in a straight line at 480 km/h. _____

   (c) A bicycle slowing from 20 km/h to a stop for a stop sign. _____

   (d) A skydiver falling freely after jumping from an airplane. _____

2. Anwar places a ball on the floor of the school bus and holds it in at rest with respect to the bus. The bus is moving in a straight line at 60 km/h when he removes his hand from the ball. After a few seconds, the driver applies the brakes, slows the bus to 40 km/h, and then, continues at 40 km/h. Describe the expected motion of the ball relative to the bus. K/U C A

3. A bale of hay with a mass of 5.00 kg is placed on a flatbed truck that has a maximum acceleration of 3.20 m/s^2. The coefficient of static friction between the hay and the bed of the truck is 0.448. Will the hay slide off the back of the truck as it accelerates down the road? Provide calculations to support your answer. T/I C A

MAIN IDEA: Fictitious forces help explain motion in a non-inertial frame of reference. Apparent weight is the magnitude of the normal force acting on an object in a non-inertial frame of reference.

4. Selena was riding her motorcycle at 10 km/h in a parking lot when she struck a concrete barrier. Later, she said, "The force of the collision threw me over the handlebars and onto the pavement." Comment on her statement in terms of frames of reference. K/U T/I C

5. Raleigh has a mass of 60.0 kg and is standing on a scale in an elevator. The scale reads 750 N. Describe the motion of the elevator. Provide calculations to support your answer. K/U T/I C A

6. A ball is tied to a string and suspended from the ceiling of an airplane, ready for takeoff on a runway. The airplane accelerates down the runway at 3.36 m/s^2 [forward]. What angle does the string make with the horizontal? T/I

3.1 Inertial and Non-inertial Frames of Reference **33**

Centripetal Acceleration

Textbook pp. 114–119

Vocabulary	
uniform circular motion	period (T)
centripetal acceleration ($\vec{a}_c$)	frequency (f)

MAIN IDEA: Uniform circular motion is the motion of any body that follows a circular path at a constant speed. Centripetal acceleration is the instantaneous acceleration of an object toward the centre of a circular path.

STUDY **TIP**

Common Error
A common error is to assume that a body moving at a constant speed is not accelerating. Circular motion results in acceleration due to constantly changing direction of the velocity vector, although its length does indeed remain constant.

1. Which of these bodies are undergoing centripetal acceleration? K/U
   (a) A child rides one of the wooden horses around a carousel.
   (b) An airplane is flown in a circular vertical loop.
   (c) A car makes a turn to the left following a quarter circle path.
   (d) all of the above

2. Is the following statement true or false? If you think the statement is false, rewrite it to make it true: A body moving in a circular path at a constant speed is not accelerating. K/U

3. Explain how it is possible that a body with a constant speed can be accelerating. Illustrate your answer with a sketch. K/U C A

MAIN IDEA: There are three equations to determine centripetal acceleration:

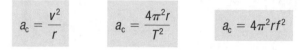

$$a_c = \frac{v^2}{r} \qquad a_c = \frac{4\pi^2 r}{T^2} \qquad a_c = 4\pi^2 r f^2$$

4. A motorcycle is driven at 20.0 m/s around a circular portion of track that has a radius of 60.0 m. What is the centripetal acceleration of the motorcycle? T/I A

5. A Ferris wheel has a radius of 8.20 m and completes a turn in 20.0 s. Determine the centripetal acceleration of one of the riders. T/I A

6. A DVD player is spinning a DVD at 632 revolutions per minute (rpm). The radius of the disc is 6.10 cm. What is the centripetal acceleration of a point on the outer edge of the disc? T/I A

Centripetal Force

Textbook pp. 120–124

> **Vocabulary**
>
> centripetal force (F_c)

MAIN IDEA: An object moving with uniform circular motion experiences a net force directed toward the centre of the object's circular path. The net force that causes uniform circular motion is the centripetal force, which may comprise one or more other forces such as gravity, the normal force, or tension.

STUDY TIP

Draw a Diagram
Sometimes it helps to draw a diagram of the problem so you can visualize it.

1. Basiruddin is standing on the outer edge of the merry-go-round at the park. As it rotates, he waits until he is due east of the centre of the ride, at which time his instantaneous velocity is pointing north. In which direction will he tend to fall? Explain your answer. K/U T/I

2. Letta is driving her car on an icy road when she enters a circular curve of constant radius. She finds that she cannot keep the car on the road, and slides off onto the shoulder. Why does this occur? T/I A

3. Indicate whether each statement is true or false. If you think a statement is false, rewrite it to make it true. K/U

   (a) A fixed-radius curve on a highway can be banked such that a car will follow a circular path. This can occur even if snow or ice reduces the static friction between the tires and the road close to zero.

   (b) As the radius of the circular path increases, the centripetal acceleration decreases.

   (c) The Moon does not undergo centripetal acceleration because it is moving at a constant speed.

MAIN IDEA: Combine the equation for Newton's second law of motion with the equations for centripetal acceleration to calculate the magnitude of the net force:

$$\sum F = ma_c \qquad F_c = \frac{mv^2}{r}$$

4. A rotating swing ride at a theme park moves riders on the outside row of swings at a speed of 4.36 m/s. Such a rider has a mass of 52.0 kg and is 6.42 m from the centre of the rotation. What centripetal force is needed to keep the rider moving in a circle? K/U T/I

5. An airplane turns by banking the wings such that the lift of the wings has a component in the direction of the centre of the turn. A pilot wishes to turn the aircraft in a radius of 800.0 m while flying at a constant speed of 55.6 m/s. Determine the angle of bank needed, measured from the vertical. K/U T/I

Rotating Frames of Reference

Vocabulary

centrifuge

centrifugal force

Coriolis force

artificial gravity

MAIN IDEA: A centrifuge is a device that spins rapidly and is used to separate substances by density, as well as simulate the effects of gravity. When a centrifuge spins it applies a force to the objects it contains. A rotating frame of reference is the frame of reference of any object moving in a circle.

1. How can a centrifuge be used? K/U
   (a) to separate solid particles like fine sand from water
   (b) to simulate gravity
   (c) to train jet pilots to withstand high-g operations
   (d) all of the above

2. Karyn says, "A centrifuge can produce artificial gravity greater than the acceleration due to gravity at the surface of Earth (9.8 m/s^2)." Is she correct? Explain. K/U

MAIN IDEA: Centrifugal force is a fictitious force used to explain the outward force observed in a rotating frame of reference. The fictitious force that acts perpendicular to the velocity of an object or particle in a rotating frame of reference is called the Coriolis force.

3. A ball is placed on the floor of a carousel that is rotating with a period of 40.0 s. The ball is released. From the point of view of a rider on the carousel, what will the ball appear to do? Explain your answer. K/U A
   (a) stay at the point it was placed
   (b) move toward the outer edge of the carousel at a constant speed
   (c) accelerate toward the outer edge of the carousel
   (d) accelerate toward the centre of rotation

> **STUDY TIP**
>
> **Word Origin**
> Many words have a common stem. The stem has a certain meaning. For example, *centri* means "centre." By breaking words down into parts and giving meaning to each part, you can derive a definition for the word.

4. A jet pilot must withstand up to $10g$ accelerations during normal operations of a fighter jet. A centrifuge is built to simulate this effect on the ground. The radius of rotation is 20.0 m. How fast must the pilot be moving such that the apparent gravitational acceleration from his point of view is $10g$? Include diagrams with your answer. T/I C A

5. A space station is built in a circular form with a radius of 25.0 m, and rotates with a period of 10.0 s. A cross-passage is built from a point on the station directly through the centre to join the opposite side of the station. What is the apparent gravity experienced by an astronaut in the passage halfway toward the centre of the station? T/I A

Physics JOURNAL

Textbook pp. 131–132

The Physics of Roller Coasters

MAIN IDEA: A roller coaster uses loops to increase the thrill of the ride. Vertical loops require a minimum speed at the top to ensure that the car does not leave the track. The minimum speed can be calculated from the equation $v = \sqrt{gr}$. The clothoid loop is preferred over the circular loop because it lessens sudden changes in normal force as the car goes around the loop.

1. Sketch and label a clothoid loop. Explain how the clothoid differs from the circular loop. **K/U** **C**

STUDY TIP

Use the Internet
If you have not experienced a loop on a roller coaster, you can watch video clips to get an idea of what it looks like. Search the Internet using the keywords "roller coaster."

2. A roller coaster car goes around a vertical loop at the minimum speed possible. Which statement is true about the car at the top of the loop? Explain your answer. **K/U** **T/I**
   (a) The speed of the car is zero.
   (b) The normal force of the track on the car is zero.
   (c) The normal force equals the gravitational force in magnitude.
   (d) The occupants feel heavier than normal.

3. A roller coaster car moves around a vertical clothoid loop at a speed of 20.0 m/s. What is the maximum possible radius at the top of the loop that will prevent the car from leaving the track? **T/I** **A**

Explore an Issue in Dynamics

Improvements in Athletic Technology

Textbook pp. 133–134

MAIN IDEA: Athletic performance depends on physical abilities, but also on technical equipment, medicine, and nutrition. Advances in clothing and equipment technologies have led to increases in performance.

1. Use a graphic organizer to illustrate how at least six professions, other than athlete, contribute to improvements in sports performance. K/U C

2. Which of the following might affect records set in track and field events? Use physics terms to explain how each affects athletic performance.
   (a) replacement of grass with synthetic materials
   (b) new fabrics for athletic clothing
   (c) new materials for running shoes
   (d) all of the above

Uniform Circular Motion

Use the graphic organizer below to summarize what you have learned about uniform circular motion. Add arrows to show the connection between the concepts. You can add your own notes, diagrams, and equations to this graphic organizer, creating a study tool to help you review Chapter 3.

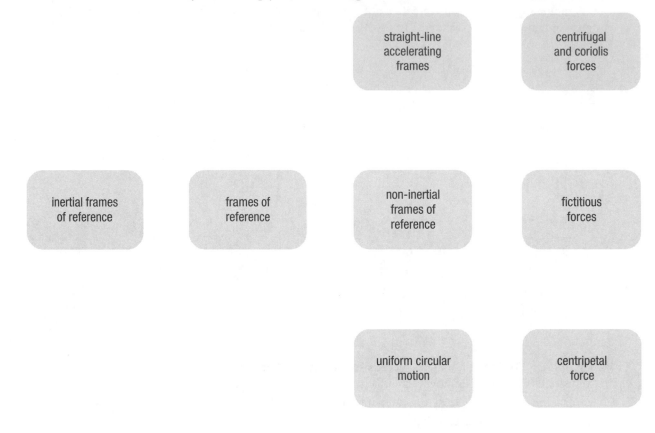

1. Katja is standing on a scale in an elevator that is moving upward at a constant speed of 3.00 m/s. The scale reads 480 N. The cable suspending the elevator fails, and the elevator goes into free fall for two seconds before the emergency brakes deploy. During free fall, what will the scale read? (3.1) K/U
   (a) more than 480
   (b) less than 480 N but not 0 N
   (c) 480 N
   (d) 0 N

2. A constant-radius curve on a highway is banked assuming a speed of 100 km/h and a radius of 200 m. If the speed limit on the highway is increased before the curve is constructed, what change(s) should be made to the plans? (3.3) K/U
   (a) Increase the radius of the curve.
   (b) Increase the bank angle.
   (c) Decrease the bank angle.
   (d) Both (a) and (c).

3. Indicate whether each statement is true or false. If you think the statement is false, rewrite it to make it true. K/U
   (a) A bicycle tire is cut in half to form a circular half-pipe. A marble is set rolling around the pipe. The walls of the pipe exert a force on the marble to move it along a circular path. (3.2)

   (b) A restaurant at the top of the Skylon Tower in Niagara Falls slowly rotates so that diners can enjoy a changing view of the Falls. Diners do not feel a Coriolis force because they are at rest with respect to the restaurant. (3.4)

   (c) Modern roller coasters use clothoid loops rather than circular loops to decrease the minimum speed required at the top of the loop. (3.5)

   (d) Advances in sports technology have had no measureable effect on records set in track and field events over the last century. (3.6)

4. A book was placed on a table in a camper van. The coefficient of friction between the book and the table was 0.162. What is the maximum acceleration that the driver can achieve without the book sliding off the table? (3.1) T/I A

K/U Knowledge/Understanding
T/I Thinking/Investigation
C Communication
A Application

5. The propeller of an airplane has a radius of 97.2 cm and is spinning at 2101 revolutions per minute (rpm). What is the centripetal acceleration of a point at the tip of the propeller? (3.2) T/I A

6. Alana is riding her bicycle at 3.60 m/s. The total mass of Alana and the bicycle is 65.0 kg. She turns to the right following a circular path of radius 9.00 m. To do so, she leans the bicycle at an angle of 11.0° from the vertical. Complete the following, and include diagrams in your answers. (3.3) T/I C A
   (a) Determine the force exerted by the road on the bicycle.

   (b) Explain how this force arises in terms of components.

7. The Tilt-a-Whirl ride at a theme park consists of a large cylinder that starts rotating horizontally. The riders are "forced" against the inside walls of the cylinder as the ride gains speed. Then, the ride slowly tilts until it reaches a vertical position. The ride has a radius of 5.62 m. What is the minimum period of the ride that ensures that no rider falls off at the top of the circle? (3.4) T/I A

8. Design a physics problem involving a body in a non-inertial frame of reference. Provide a full worked solution to your problem. Use a separate sheet of paper. (3.1, 3.2, 3.3, 3.4) T/I C A

9. The track at the bottom of the first "drop" on a roller coaster is in the shape of a quarter circle with a radius of 12.0 m. A rider feels twice his normal weight at the lowest point. What is the speed of the coaster at this point? (3.6) T/I C A

1. Marla ties a ball on a string and twirls it around her in a horizontal circle. The ball moves at a constant speed of v m/s. The ball covers the quarter circle from due north of Marla to due east of Marla in 1.00 s. What is the average acceleration of the ball? (1.4) K/U A

   (a) 0 m/s^2 [S of W]
   (b) v m/s^2 [S of W]
   (c) v m/s^2 [S of E]
   (d) $\sqrt{2}v$ m/s^2 [S of W]

2. A skier is standing facing down a hill, but does not move. She gives herself a push with her poles to start moving. Although she stops pushing, she continues to move down the hill. Why does she not stop again? (2.4) K/U A

   (a) The kinetic friction opposing her motion down the hill is less than the component of gravity directed down the hill.
   (b) The static friction stopping her from beginning the slide is weaker than the kinetic friction when she is moving.
   (c) The component of gravity perpendicular to the hill keeps her moving.
   (d) The normal force of the snow on the skis is greater than the kinetic friction opposing her motion down the hill.

3. Which is a fictitious force? (3.4) K/U

   (a) the normal force
   (b) the Coriolis force
   (c) the centripetal force
   (d) All of these.

4. Evaluate each explanation and decide whether it is correct or incorrect. If you think the explanation is incorrect, explain your reasoning. K/U

   (a) A graph of velocity versus time for a bicycle moving east slopes downwards to the right in a straight line. The cyclist is slowing the bicycle with a constant acceleration. (1.1)

   (b) A horse pulls a wagon forward. This is possible because the force exerted by the horse on the wagon is greater than the force exerted by the wagon on the horse. (2.2)

   (c) A car is heading north on an icy road at 90 km/h. It reaches a banked curve designed for a speed of 80 km/h, turning towards the west. If the ice results in a zero coefficient of friction between the tires and the road, the car will go off the road to the driver's left. (3.3)

5. A soccer player kicks a ball which is initially at rest towards the west. While in contact with his foot, the ball experiences an average acceleration of 8.60 m/s^2 [W] over a distance of 0.824 m. What is the final velocity of the ball? (1.2) T/I A

6. A football player kicks a football with a speed of 15.0 m/s at an angle of 40.0° above the horizontal. A team member catches the ball at the same height above the grass that it was kicked. What is the horizontal distance between the kicker and the catcher? (1.5) T/I A

7. A tetherball with a mass of 243 g is hanging on a rope. A wind comes up and blows the ball sideways such that the rope makes an angle of 14.0° with the vertical. Determine the magnitude of the tension in the rope. (2.1) T/I A

8. An airplane makes an emergency landing in a grass field. The coefficient of kinetic friction between the plane and the ground is 0.644. If the plane touches down at a speed of 40.0 m/s, how far will it slide before coming to a stop? (1.2, 2.4) T/I A

9. Sandor fills a bucket with water, and whirls it in a vertical circle to demonstrate that the water will not spill from the bucket as long as he maintains a minimum speed at the top of the loop. If the length of the rope from his hand to the centre of the bucket is 1.24 m, what is the minimum tension in the rope at the top of the swing? Explain your answer. (3.4) T/I

10. An aerobatic pilot performs a vertical loop with a radius of 400.0 m. As she takes the plane through the bottom of the loop, she feels three times her normal weight at the lowest point. What is the speed of the airplane at this point? (3.3) T/I C A

Energy and Momentum

Chapter 4: Work and Energy

Work occurs when a force, $\vec{F}$, is applied to move an object, causing a displacement, $\Delta\vec{d}$. The work done on an object (in joules, J) is given by $W = F\Delta d \cos\theta$, where θ is the angle between $\vec{F}$ and $\vec{d}$. A force does zero work on an object when the angle between the force and the object's displacement is $90°$. Zero work is also done when either the force or the displacement is zero.

Kinetic energy, E_k, is the energy an object has due to its motion and is calculated using the equation $E_k = \dfrac{1}{2}mv^2$, where m is the object's mass and v is its speed. The total work done is given by $W = \Delta E_k$.

Potential energy is the stored energy of an object that can be released into another form of energy. Mechanical energy is the sum of kinetic and potential energies. Gravitational potential energy is the energy an object has due to its height above a reference point (Δy) and can be calculated by using the equation $\Delta E_g = mg\Delta y$, where m is the mass of the object and g is the acceleration due to gravity.

The law of conservation of energy states that energy can neither be created nor destroyed in an isolated system; it can only change form. Power is the rate of work done during a time interval, or the rate at which the energy of a system changes.

Hooke's law states that the force exerted by a spring (or, equivalently, the force applied to a spring) is given by $\vec{F} = -k\Delta\vec{x}$, where k is the spring constant, in newtons per metre, and $\Delta\vec{x}$ is the displacement of the spring from its equilibrium position.

The elastic potential energy of an object that has been stretched, compressed, or bent is $E_e = \dfrac{1}{2}k(\Delta x)^2$. Simple harmonic motion is periodic motion due to an object's response to a force that is directionally proportional and opposite to its displacement.

Chapter 5: Momentum and Collisions

Linear momentum is the product of an object's mass and its velocity, expressed in units of kilograms times metres per second (kg·m/s): $\vec{p} = m\vec{v}$. Impulse is the change in momentum caused by the application of a force over a time interval, expressed in newton seconds (N·s): $\vec{F}\Delta t = \Delta\vec{p}$.

The change in momentum of one object is equal in magnitude but opposite in direction to that of the other object: $m_1\vec{v}_{i_1} + m_2\vec{v}_{i_2} = m_1\vec{v}_{f_1} + m_2\vec{v}_{f_2}$, where m is the mass of the objects and v is their respective velocities before and after the interaction.

When analyzing elastic and inelastic collisions, use the conservation of kinetic energy, $\dfrac{1}{2}m_1v_{i_1}^2 + \dfrac{1}{2}m_2v_{i_2}^2 = \dfrac{1}{2}m_1v_{f_1}^2 + \dfrac{1}{2}m_2v_{f_2}^2$ and the conservation of momentum, $m_1\vec{v}_{i_1} + m_2\vec{v}_{i_2} = m_1\vec{v}_{f_1} + m_2\vec{v}_{f_2}$.

The laws of conservation of momentum and conservation of kinetic energy for collisions in one- or two-dimensions are the same. Momentum is conserved for elastic and inelastic collisions. Kinetic energy is conserved only in elastic collisions.

BIG IDEAS

- Energy and momentum are conserved in all interactions.
- Interactions involving the laws of conservation of energy and conservation of momentum can be analyzed mathematically.
- Technological applications that involve energy and momentum can affect society and the environment in positive and negative ways.

Work Done by a Constant Force

Textbook pp. 164–170

MAIN IDEA: Work occurs when a force, $\vec{F}$, acts upon an object to cause a displacement, $\Delta\vec{d}$. Only the component of the force that acts parallel to the direction of motion does work. The component of the force acting perpendicular to the displacement does no work.

1. Describe a situation in which work, in the scientific sense of the word, is done. Explain why work is done. K/U C A

2. Describe a situation in which a person exerts effort but no work is done. Explain why no work is done. K/U C A

3. The SI unit of work and energy is the _____, also called the _____. K/U

4. (a) Match the diagrams in **Figure 1** to the descriptions. K/U
   A. The displacement is in the direction of the force. _____
   B. The force and the displacement are at an angle to each other. _____
   C. The displacement is perpendicular to the force. _____

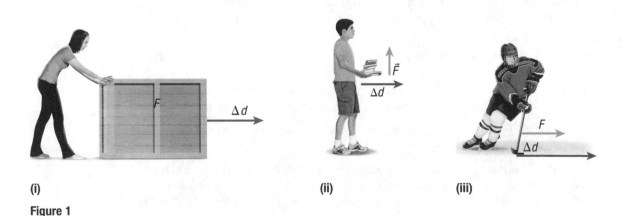

(i)   (ii)   (iii)

Figure 1

   (b) In which of the above situations is no work done? _____

MAIN IDEA: The work done on an object is given by $W = F\Delta d \cos\theta$, where F is the magnitude of the force, Δd is the magnitude of the object's displacement, and θ is the angle between the force and the displacement.

5. Fill in **Table 1** below to show the relationship between the direction of the force, the direction of the displacement, and the work done. K/U

Table 1 Force, Displacement, and Work

Force and displacement are …	Angle between force and displacement is …	Work done is …
in the same direction		positive
	between 90° and 180°	

6. A worker pushes a crate forward with a constant force of 52.0 N a distance of 6.4 m. The angle between the force and the displacement of the crate is 45°. How much work is done on the crate by the worker? T/I

STUDY TIP

Remembering Formulas
A mathematical formula is written in the form of symbols which represent physical quantities, such as displacement or force. To help you remember formulas, think about the unit for the quantity you wish to find; for example, the unit of work is the joule, which is a newton-metre. The newton is the unit for force and the metre is the unit of distance/displacement.

MAIN IDEA: When an object moves in a direction opposite to an applied force, the force does negative work on the object.

7. A train is moving along a straight track when the driver suddenly applies the brakes. The force of friction between the wheels and the tracks is opposite to the train's direction of motion and decreases the train's speed. Calculate the work done by a constant frictional force of 2.3 kN over a distance of 5.7×10^2 m. T/I

8. Negative work will cause a loss of _____ energy. K/U

MAIN IDEA: When an object moves at an angle to an applied force, only the component of the force in the direction of the displacement does work on the object.

9. When analyzing the total work done on an object, _____ forces that are present, including _____, must be considered. K/U

10. A husky pulls a sled 520 m with a constant force of 95 N exerted at a 12° angle to the sled's displacement. At the same time, a constant 58.0 N frictional force on the sled from the snow opposes the motion. K/U T/I

    (a) What other forces are acting on the sled? Do these forces contribute to the work?

    (b) Calculate the work done on the sled by the husky.

    (c) Calculate the work done on the sled by friction.

    (d) Calculate the total work done on the sled.

11. Complete the statement using the terms "force" and "displacement".
    The three situations in which zero work is done are when the
    _____, the _____, or the cosine of the angle
    between the _____ and the _____ is zero. K/U

Kinetic Energy and the Work–Energy Theorem

Textbook pp. 171–176

Vocabulary

kinetic energy (E_k)   work–energy theorem

MAIN IDEA: Kinetic energy, E_k, is the energy an object has due to its motion. It is a scalar quantity because no direction is associated with it. The units of kinetic energy are joules (J). An object's kinetic energy is related to its mass, m, and its speed, v, by the equation $E_k = \dfrac{1}{2}mv^2$.

1. The units of kinetic energy are the same as the units of _____. The units of kinetic energy are _____. K/U

2. Restate the kinetic energy equation in your own words. K/U C

> **STUDY TIP**
>
> **Restating Equations**
> When you read an equation, restating it in more familiar language can help you better understand and remember the relationship that the equation represents.

3. Is kinetic energy a vector or scalar quantity? Use an example to explain. K/U T/I

4. A car travelling at 73.6 km/h has 5.15×10^5 J of kinetic energy. What is the mass of the car? T/I

> **STUDY TIP**
>
> **Analyzing Problems**
> Look at the problems you solved in a section or chapter and classify each problem according to its method of solution. Is it a force, displacement, and work problem? A kinetic energy problem? A work–energy problem?

MAIN IDEA: According to the work–energy theorem, the total work done on an object is equal to the change in the object's kinetic energy: $W = \Delta E_k$.

5. A 75 kg swimmer is swimming laps at a speed of 2.6 m/s. On his last lap, he speeds up to 3.6 m/s. Calculate the work done on the swimmer by the water. **T/I**

6. A skateboarder with a mass of 57.5 kg increases her speed to 3.80 m/s as she rolls down a ramp. The increase in speed results in 342 J of work done on the skateboard. Determine the initial speed of the skateboarder. **T/I**

7. (a) What assumption is commonly made when using the work–energy theorem?

   (b) Is this assumption correct in all real-world situations? Explain why or why not. **K/U** **T/I** **A**

Gravitational Potential Energy

Textbook pp. 177–181

Vocabulary		
potential energy	mechanical energy	gravitational potential energy (E_g)

MAIN IDEA: Potential energy is the stored energy an object has that can be converted into another form of energy. Mechanical energy is the sum of an object's kinetic and potential energies. Gravitational potential energy is the energy that an object has due to its height above a reference point. It is a scalar quantity and is measured in joules (J). When solving problems related to gravitational potential energy, choose a reference point, $y = 0$, from which to measure the gravitational potential energy.

1. Describe a situation in which potential energy is converted to another form of energy. `C` `A`

2. Define "reference point" in your own words. `K/U` `C`

3. An object's gravitational potential energy value when it is at the reference point is _____. `K/U`

4. A ball is dropped from the roof of a five-storey building to a second-floor balcony. What you would choose as the reference point for gravitational potential energy? Explain why. `K/U` `C`

5. At a given moment, a pencil falling to the floor has 9.0 J of kinetic energy and 16 J of gravitational potential energy. The mechanical energy of the pencil is _____. `T/I`

MAIN IDEA: The gravitational potential energy of an object near Earth's surface depends on the object's mass, m; the acceleration due to gravity, g; and the object's change in height as measured from a reference height, Δy: $\Delta E_g = mg\Delta y$.

6. Fill in **Table 1** below to explain what is indicated by each part of the equation $\Delta E_g = mg\Delta y$. `K/U`

Table 1 Variables for Gravitational Potential Energy

Variable	Meaning	SI Unit
ΔE_g	change in gravitational potential energy of object	J
m		
g		
Δy		

Visualizing Problems
When working out a problem, try to
visualize what it is asking you to do.
Sketch a diagram, then identify the
variables and set up the equation.

7. A drop-tower ride lifts its gondola and riders up 78.0 m from the base of the tower. The gondola and riders have a combined mass of 450.0 kg. What is their change in gravitational potential energy? T/I

8. A pulley exerts a vertical force of 3670 N to lift a crate to a height of 32.7 m above its original position. The lift increases the crate's gravitational potential energy by 1.20×10^5 J. T/I

(a) How much work did the force do on the crate? Compare this to the gain in the crate's gravitational potential energy.

(b) Determine the mass of the crate.

Explore an Issue in Energy Generation

Gravitational Potential Energy and Hydroelectricity

Textbook pp. 182–183

MAIN IDEA: Hydroelectric power uses the kinetic energy of moving water to produce electricity. Hydroelectric power is a renewable and relatively green energy source; however, there are drawbacks to using this source of power.

1. Organize what you know about hydroelectric power by filling in the main ideas web below. C A

What are the environmental advantages?

What are the environmental drawbacks?

Hydroelectric

What are the economic social advantages?

What are the economic or social drawbacks?

The Law of Conservation of Energy

> **Vocabulary**
>
> isolated system   open system   biochemical energy   power

MAIN IDEA: The law of conservation of energy states that energy can neither be created nor destroyed in an isolated system; it can only change form. An isolated, or closed, system cannot interact with other systems or exchange energy with its surroundings. However, an open system can exchange energy with its surroundings.

1. Use **Figure 1** to explain the relationship between the potential, kinetic, and mechanical energy of a roller coaster car as it moves along the track. K/U C

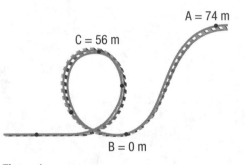

A = 74 m
C = 56 m
B = 0 m

Figure 1

2. A roller coaster car and its passengers have a mass of 755 kg. The roller coaster track is frictionless. The car passes point A in Figure 1 at 0.230 m/s and travels to point C. K/U T/I

   (a) Calculate the mechanical energy of the car at point A.

(b) What is the kinetic energy of the train at point B?

(c) Work is done as the roller coaster car accelerates down the track. What force does the work?

3. Total energy is always conserved, but the mechanical energy in a system may not be conserved. Explain why. K/U

4. (a) Define "biochemical energy" in your own words.

(b) Give an example of a biochemical energy conversion other than photosynthesis. K/U C A

MAIN IDEA: Power is the rate at which work is done during a time interval, or the rate at which the energy of a system changes.

5. Use the work–energy theorem to write an equation for power as the rate of change of energy. K/U T/I

6. The unit of power is a _____ per second, or _____.
   A car with a power rating of 70 kW requires 70 _____ of energy
   per _____ when running. K/U

7. A 450 kg horse runs a 400.0 m race at an average speed of 85.0 km/h. Calculate the power the horse exerts. T/I

Elastic Potential Energy and Simple Harmonic Motion

Textbook pp. 192–200

Vocabulary

Hooke's law	electrical potential energy	period (T)
spring constant (k)	amplitude (A)	frequency (f)
ideal spring	simple harmonic motion	

MAIN IDEA: Hooke's law states that the force exerted by a spring (or, equivalently, the force applied to a spring) is directly proportional to the spring's displacement from its rest equilibrium position, $\vec{F}_x = -k\Delta\vec{x}$.

1. (a) Label **Figure 1** with the following terms: equilibrium position, stretched, compressed.

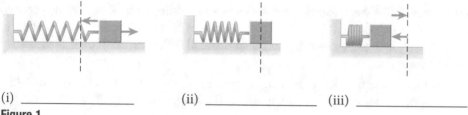

(i) _____   (ii) _____   (iii) _____

Figure 1

(b) What forces are involved in each diagram? K/U T/I

2. (a) When a spring is stretched by pulling it to the right, the force exerted by the spring is to the _____.

(b) When a spring is compressed by pushing it to the left, the force exerted by the spring is to the _____. K/U

3. A spring loses 0.5 J of energy to friction as it is stretched. Is this spring an ideal spring? Explain why or why not. K/U T/I C

4. Fill in **Table 1** below to explain the meaning of each variable in the equation $\vec{F}_x = -k\Delta\vec{x}$. K/U

Table 1 Variables for Hooke's Law

Variable	Meaning	SI Unit
$\vec{F}_x$		
k		
$\Delta\vec{x}$		

5. Indicate whether the following statements about Hooke's law are true or false. If you think the statement is false, rewrite it to make it true. K/U

(a) The stiffer the spring, the smaller the value for k and the smaller the force required to extend or compress the spring.

(b) If $\Delta \vec{x}$ is downward, then $\vec{F}_x$ is upward.

(c) There is a negative sign on the right-hand side of the Hooke's law equation because the restoring force always acts in the opposite direction to the spring constant.

MAIN IDEA: The force exerted by a spring is a restorative force. It acts in the opposite direction of the displacement to return the spring to its natural length. The constant of proportionality in Hooke's law is the spring constant, k. The spring constant is measured in newtons per metre.

6. In **Figure 1**, a 0.25 kg mass hangs at rest from a spring that is attached to a support. Draw a free-body diagram for the suspended mass. K/U T/I C

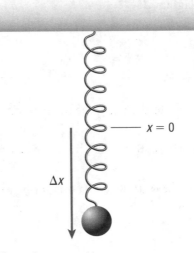

$x = 0$

Δx

Figure 1

7. A 10.7 kg mass is suspended from a strong spring with a spring constant of 63.1 N/m. Calculate the displacement, in metres, of the spring. T/I

MAIN IDEA: The energy stored in an object that is stretched, compressed, twisted, or bent is called elastic potential energy, $E_e = \dfrac{1}{2}k(\Delta x)^2$.

8. A spring is stretched to its position 2.50 m from its equilibrium position. The spring constant is 20.0 N/m. Calculate the elastic potential energy stored in the spring. `T/I`

9. A spring is stretched to its position 0.95 m from its equilibrium position. The spring constant is 11.5 N/m. Calculate the elastic potential energy stored in the spring. `T/I`

MAIN IDEA: Simple harmonic motion (SHM) is periodic motion in which the acceleration of the object is directly proportional and opposite to its displacement.

10. Identify an example of SHM from daily life. `C` `A`

11. A mass is attached to an ideal spring on a horizontal frictionless surface. The mass–spring system oscillates with a period of 4.0 s. The spring constant is 40.0 N/m. Calculate the mass of the spring and the frequency at which the spring oscillates. `T/I`

4.7

Springs and Conservation of Energy

Textbook pp. 201–207

Vocabulary

perpetual motion machine | damped harmonic motion

MAIN IDEA: For an isolated mass–spring system, the total mechanical energy—kinetic energy, elastic potential energy, and gravitational potential energy—remains constant.

1. A model car of mass 2.7 kg is released from a height of 1.6 m. It slides down a frictionless ramp into a spring with spring constant 3.1 kN/m at a speed of 4.7 m/s (**Figure 1**). Calculate the distance the spring has been compressed. T/I

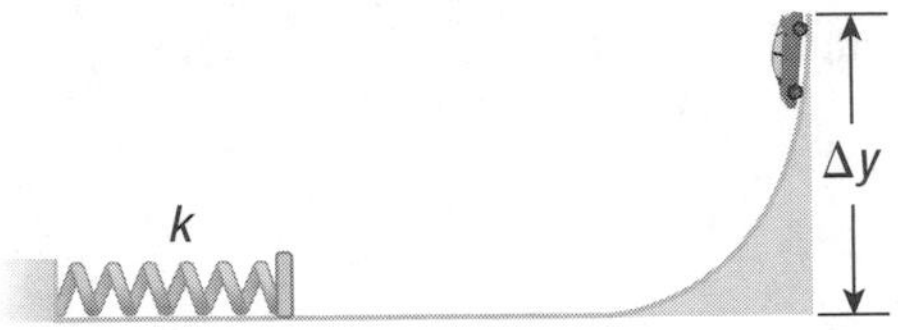

Figure 1

2. A block is held against a spring, compressing the spring (**Figure 2**). After the block is released, it travels along a frictionless horizontal surface and then up a frictionless ramp. K/U T/I

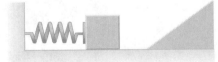

Figure 2

(a) Describe the energy transformations as the block travels along the horizontal surface and up the ramp.

(b) Explain why mechanical energy is conserved throughout this problem.

MAIN IDEA: A perpetual motion machine is a machine than can operate forever without restarting or refuelling. Damped harmonic motion is periodic motion in which friction causes a decrease in the amplitude of motion and the total mechanical energy.

3. (a) Explain why a real-world perpetual motion machine can never be built.

   (b) Why is a spring undergoing simple harmonic motion for over an hour not considered a perpetual motion machine? K/U

4. Complete **Table 1** with descriptions and examples of the three categories of damped motion. K/U C A

Table 1 The Three Categories of Damped Motion

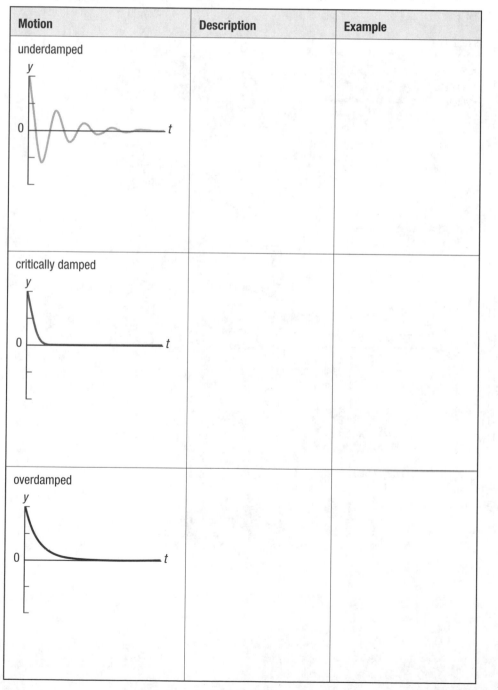

Motion	Description	Example
underdamped		
critically damped		
overdamped		

4.7 Springs and Conservation of Energy   **63**

Work and Energy

Energy can be released to form another type of energy. It cannot be created or destroyed. When a force acts on an object causing a displacement, work is done. Use the graphic organizer below to summarize what you have learned about work, energy, and periodic motion. You can add your own notes, diagrams, and equations to this graphic organizer, creating a study tool to help you review Chapter 4.

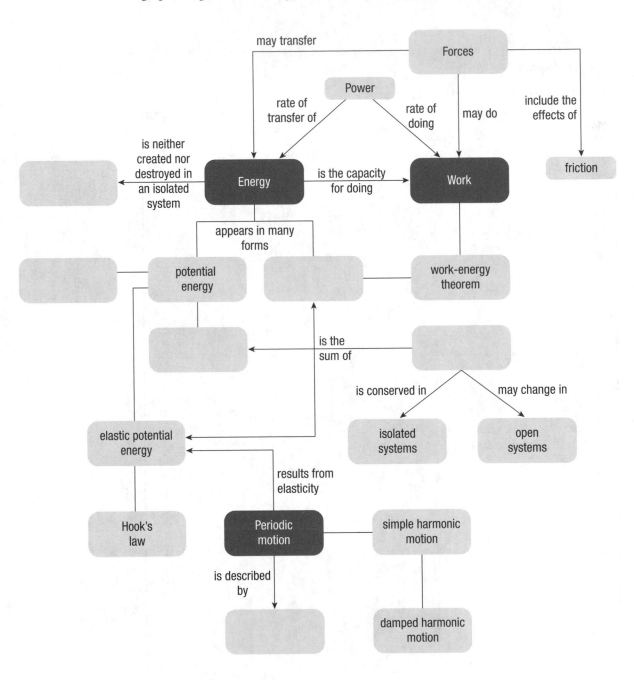

1. A force does not do work on an object when the object's displacement is

   (a) in the same direction as the force
   (b) at an angle between 0° and 90° to the force
   (c) perpendicular to the force
   (d) in the opposite direction to the force (4.1) K/U

2. The work–energy theorem shows that doing work on an object changes its
   (a) kinetic energy
   (b) gravitational potential energy
   (c) elastic potential energy
   (d) mechanical energy (4.2) K/U

3. Indicate whether each statement is true or false. If you think the statement is false, rewrite it to make it true. K/U
   (a) Work and energy are vector quantities. The unit of work and energy is the newton. (4.1, 4.2)

   (b) In the equation $W = F\Delta d \cos \theta$, $\cos \theta$ is positive for angles between 90° and 180°. (4.1)

   (c) The total work done on an object is the sum of the work done by the individual forces. (4.1)

   (d) Potential energy is the energy an object has because of its motion. (4.2)

4. You know the mass and the initial and final speeds of an object. Explain how you would use the kinetic energy equation and the work–energy theorem to calculate the work done on the object. (4.2) T/I C

5. A 25 kg box of shingles is lifted 6.8 m to the roof of a house. (4.3) T/I A
   (a) Determine the work done on the shingles to get them on the roof.

   (b) A smaller package of shingles requires only one fifth of the work to lift it up to the roof. What is the mass of the smaller package?

6. Describe a new technology related to modern hydroelectric power generation and identify one advantage and one disadvantage of using this technology to generate electricity. (4.4) C A

7. Describe the transformations of gravitational potential, kinetic, and elastic potential energies in a diver as he climbs the ladder of a diving tower, jumps on the diving board, dives, and hits the water. Treat the diver as an isolated system; ignore influences such as air friction and the energy of vibrations in the diving board. (4.5, 4.7) K/U C A

8. Design a physics problem that you would solve using Hooke's law. Provide a full worked solution to your problem. (4.6) T/I A

9. The spring constant for an ideal spring is 350 N/m. Calculate how far you must stretch the spring from its equilibrium position in order to store 27.0 J of elastic potential energy in it. (4.6, 4.7) T/I

Momentum and Impulse

Vocabulary	
linear momentum ($\vec{p}$)	Impulse

Textbook pp. 222–227

MAIN IDEA: Linear momentum is the product of an object's mass and its velocity: $\vec{p} = m\vec{v}$.

1. Indicate whether the following statement is true or false. If you think the statement is false, rewrite it to make it true. Since mass is a scalar quantity, momentum is also a scalar. K/U

2. A ping-pong ball and a bowling ball are rolled along the floor with the same velocity. Which has more momentum? Explain. K/U C

3. Calculate the momentum of each bird. T/I
   (a) a 32 g sparrow flying east at 15 m/s
   (b) a 0.32 kg pigeon flying east at 15 m/s

> **STUDY TIP**
>
> **Thinking Proportionally**
> Momentum is directly proportional to both mass and velocity. Thinking and reasoning proportionally about quantities allows you to predict how a change in one variable would affect another variable.

MAIN IDEA: Impulse is the change in momentum of an object when a force is applied to the object over a time interval: $\vec{F}\Delta t = \Delta\vec{p}$.

4. Indicate whether each statement is true or false. If you think the statement is false, rewrite it to make it true. K/U
   (a) Impulse is the product of force and time.

   (b) The direction of an impulse is the same as the direction of the total force.

5. The application of a force over a specified period of time can change the _____ of an object. The application of a force over a period of time is called an _____. K/U

6. (a) Fill in the missing variables.

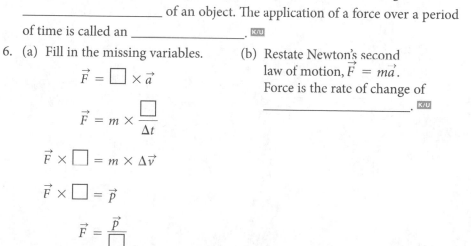

$$\vec{F} = \boxed{} \times \vec{a}$$

$$\vec{F} = m \times \frac{\boxed{}}{\Delta t}$$

$$\vec{F} \times \boxed{} = m \times \Delta\vec{v}$$

$$\vec{F} \times \boxed{} = \vec{p}$$

$$\vec{F} = \frac{\vec{p}}{\boxed{}}$$

   (b) Restate Newton's second law of motion, $\vec{F} = m\vec{a}$. Force is the rate of change of _____. K/U

7. Complete the flow chart.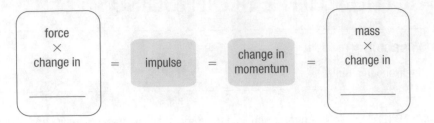

8. Calculate the change in momentum in each situation. T/I
   (a) a 60 kg cyclist puts on his brakes to slow down from 6.0 m/s to 4.0 m/s [N]

   (b) a 30 kg cyclist puts on her brakes to slow down from 8 m/s to 4 m/s [N]

9. An 80 kg hockey player hits a puck with a mass of 160 g with an average force of 30 N. If the puck is initially at rest and it moves off with a speed of 40 m/s, for how long did the force act on the puck? T/I A

MAIN IDEA: The magnitude and direction of an impulse can be determined if the direction of the force is given. The magnitude of an impulse can be found by measuring the area under a force–time curve.

10. Use the force–time graph to determine the impulse between 0 and 2.0 s. T/I C

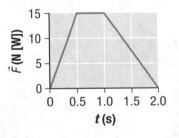

Figure 1

Conservation of Momentum in One Dimension

Textbook pp. 228–232

Vocabulary

collision   explosion

MAIN IDEA: When two or more objects collide, the change in momentum of one object is equal in magnitude but opposite in direction to that of the other object.

1. (a) State Newton's third law.

   (b) Two objects collide. Let the force exerted on object 1 by object 2 be $\vec{F}_{12}$ and the force exerted on object 2 by object 1 be $\vec{F}_{21}$. What does Newton's third law tell us about the magnitude and direction of $\vec{F}_{12}$ and $\vec{F}_{21}$? **T/I**

2. When two objects are in contact, the objects will have a common surface of contact and the objects will exert a _____ force on each other.

   The time during which this force acts upon object 1 is _____ to the time during which this force acts upon object 2. **K/U**

3. Use your answers to Questions 1 and 2 to show the following:

   In a collision between object 1 and object 2, the impulse experienced by object 1 is equal in magnitude and opposite in direction to the impulse experienced by object 2: $\vec{F}_{12}\Delta t = -\vec{F}_{21}\Delta t$. **T/I**

4. Use $\Delta \vec{p} = m\Delta \vec{v}$ to write an equation to represent the following relationship:

   In a collision between object 1 and object 2, the change in momentum experienced by object 1 is equal in magnitude and opposite in direction to the change in momentum experienced by object 2. **K/U**

> **LEARNING TIP**
>
> **Conservation Laws**
> Conservation laws such as the law of conservation of momentum are powerful problem-solving tools. Because the total amount of the conserved quantity remains constant regardless of various other conditions in the system, information about these quantities is not needed to solve the problem. Conserved quantities include momentum, energy, mass, and charge.

MAIN IDEA: When two or more objects collide, the total momentum of the system is conserved.

5. Show your understanding of conservation of momentum by filling in the **Table 1**. **K/U** **T/I**

Table 1 Conservation of Momentum Before and After a Collision

Object	Momentum before collision (kg · m/s)	Momentum after collision (kg · m/s)
hockey stick	60	
hockey puck	−30	10
Total		

6. (a) Fill in **Table 2** below to explain what is indicated by each part of the equation $m_1\vec{v}_{i_1} + m_2\vec{v}_{i_2} = m_1\vec{v}_{f_1} + m_2\vec{v}_{f_2}$.

Table 2 Variables for Conservation of Momentum

Variables	Meaning	SI unit
m_1, m_2		
$\vec{v}_{i_1}$, $\vec{v}_{i_2}$		
$\vec{v}_{f_1}$, $\vec{v}_{f_2}$		

(b) State the equation $m_1\vec{v}_{i_1} + m_2\vec{v}_{i_2} = m_1\vec{v}_{f_1} + m_2\vec{v}_{f_2}$ in words. K/U T/I

7. Is the following statement is true or false? If you think the statement is false, rewrite it to make it true. Momentum is only conserved if no external forces act on the system. K/U

MAIN IDEA: In a collision, two or more objects come together. In an explosion, a single object or collection of objects separates.

8. Give an example of a collision and an example of an explosion. K/U

9. An explosion occurs in a building, sending pieces of the building flying in all directions. Compare the total momentum of the system before and after the explosion. T/I

10. A bumper car with a mass of 225 kg is moving with a velocity 18.0 km/h [W] hits a bumper car of the same mass travelling with a velocity of 9.00 km/h [E]. The two cars stick together and an instant after impact move in the same direction. Calculate the final velocity of the two bumper cars. T/I

LEARNING TIP

External Forces
Momentum is always conserved in an isolated system. Real-life systems are subject to many outside influences, such as friction and other complicated forces, which can make detecting conservation of momentum difficult.

Collisions

Vocabulary

elastic collision

perfectly elastic collision

conservation of kinetic energy

perfectly inelastic collision

inelastic collision

Textbook pp. 233–239

MAIN IDEA: In an elastic collision, both momentum and kinetic energy are conserved. In an inelastic collision, momentum is conserved but kinetic energy is not conserved.

1. Complete **Table 1**. K/U T/I

Table 1 Conservation of Momentum and Kinetic Energy in Collisions

Type of collision	Is momentum conserved?	Is kinetic energy conserved?	Example of this type of collision
elastic			
inelastic			

2. In an inelastic collision, kinetic energy is converted into other forms, such as

_____ energy and _____ energy. K/U

MAIN IDEA: In a perfectly elastic collision, momentum and kinetic energy are perfectly conserved. In a perfectly inelastic collision, momentum is perfectly conserved but kinetic energy is not conserved.

3. After two cars collide, they lock bumpers, as shown in **Figure 1** below. Explain why there is only one final velocity. K/U T/I

Figure 1

4. Complete **Table 2**. K/U

Table 2 Perfect Conservation of Momentum, and Kinetic Energy in Collisions

Type of collision	Is momentum perfectly conserved?	Is kinetic energy perfectly conserved?
elastic		
perfectly elastic		
inelastic		
perfectly inelastic		

5. Kinetic energy is conserved in a perfectly elastic collision. A partial mathematical representation of this fact is shown. Complete the equation. K/U

$$\frac{1}{2}m_1 + \frac{1}{2}m_2\vec{v}_{i_2} = m_1\vec{v}_{f_1}^2 + \frac{1}{2}m_2$$

6. In each collision shown below, $m_1 = m_2$. Identify the collisions as elastic or inelastic. Explain your reasoning using the equation $\frac{1}{2}m_1\vec{v}_{i_1}^2 + \frac{1}{2}m_2\vec{v}_{i_2}^2 = \frac{1}{2}m_1\vec{v}_{f_1}^2 + \frac{1}{2}m_2\vec{v}_{f_2}^2$. K/U T/I C

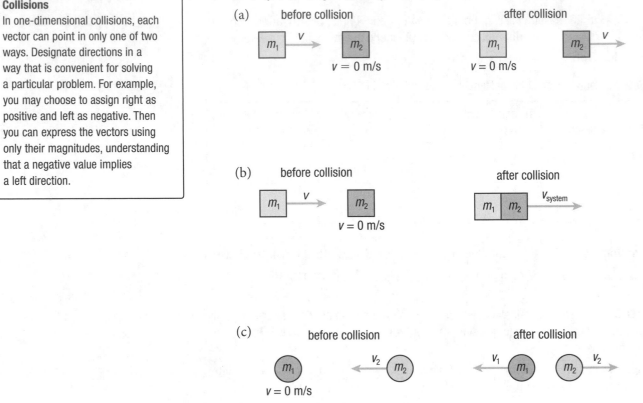

(a)   before collision   after collision

(b)   before collision   after collision

(c)   before collision   after collision

LEARNING **TIP**

Vectors in One-Dimensional Collisions

In one-dimensional collisions, each vector can point in only one of two ways. Designate directions in a way that is convenient for solving a particular problem. For example, you may choose to assign right as positive and left as negative. Then you can express the vectors using only their magnitudes, understanding that a negative value implies a left direction.

7. Write the equation that relates the final velocity of two objects in a perfectly inelastic collision to their masses and initial velocities. K/U

MAIN IDEA: When analyzing elastic and inelastic collisions, apply the equations for the conservation of kinetic energy, $\frac{1}{2}m_1\vec{v}_{i_1}^2 + \frac{1}{2}m_2\vec{v}_{i_2}^2 = \frac{1}{2}m_1\vec{v}_{f_1}^2 + \frac{1}{2}m_2\vec{v}_{f_2}^2$, and the conservation of momentum, $m_1\vec{v}_{i_1} + m_2\vec{v}_{i_2} = m_1\vec{v}_{f_1} + m_2\vec{v}_{f_2}$.

8. Describe the general strategy taken in the solution below, and explain the mathematical procedure used in each step in the solution. **T/I**

   A cue ball collides head-on with another billiard ball that is initially at rest. Both balls have the same mass. After the collision, the velocity of the ball that was hit by the cue ball is greater than zero. What are the velocities of the two balls after the collision? Assume the collision is perfectly elastic.

   Given: $m_1 = m_2 = m$; $\vec{v}_{i_1} = 0$; $\vec{v}_{f_2} > 0$

   Required: $\vec{v}_{f_1}$; $\vec{v}_{f_2}$

   Solution:

Step	Conservation of kinetic energy (Equation 1)	Conservation of momentum (Equation 2)
Original equation	$\frac{1}{2}m_1\vec{v}_{i_1}^2 + \frac{1}{2}m_2\vec{v}_{i_2}^2 = \frac{1}{2}m_1\vec{v}_{f_1}^2 + \frac{1}{2}m_2\vec{v}_{f_2}^2$	$m_1\vec{v}_{i_1} + m_2\vec{v}_{i_2} = m_1\vec{v}_{f_1} + m_2\vec{v}_{f_2}$
1	$2\left(\frac{1}{2}m_1\vec{v}_{i_1}^2 + \frac{1}{2}m_2\vec{v}_{i_2}^2 = \frac{1}{2}m_1\vec{v}_{f_1}^2 + \frac{1}{2}m_2\vec{v}_{f_2}^2\right)$ $m_1\vec{v}_{i_1}^2 + m_2\vec{v}_{i_2}^2 = m_1\vec{v}_{f_1}^2 + m_2\vec{v}_{f_2}^2$	
2	$m_1\vec{v}_{i_1}^2 + 0 = m_1\vec{v}_{f_1}^2 + m_2\vec{v}_{f_2}^2$ $m_1\vec{v}_{i_1}^2 = m_1\vec{v}_{f_1}^2 + m_2\vec{v}_{f_2}^2$	$m\vec{v}_{i_1} + 0 = m\vec{v}_{f_1} + m\vec{v}_{f_2}$ $m\vec{v}_{i_1} = m\vec{v}_{f_1} + m\vec{v}_{f_2}$
3	$m\vec{v}_{i_1}^2 = m(\vec{v}_{f_1}^2 + \vec{v}_{f_2}^2)$ $\cancel{m}\vec{v}_{i_1}^2 = \cancel{m}(\vec{v}_{f_1}^2 + \vec{v}_{f_2}^2)$ $\vec{v}_{i_1}^2 = \vec{v}_{f_1}^2 + \vec{v}_{f_2}^2$	$m\vec{v}_{i_1} = m(\vec{v}_{f_1} + \vec{v}_{f_2})$ $\cancel{m}\vec{v}_{i_1} = \cancel{m}(\vec{v}_{f_1} + \vec{v}_{f_2})$ $\vec{v}_{i_1} = \vec{v}_{f_1} + \vec{v}_{f_2}$
4		$\vec{v}_{i_1}^2 = \vec{v}_{f_1}^2 + 2\vec{v}_{f_1}\vec{v}_{f_2} + \vec{v}_{f_2}^2$
5	$\vec{v}_{i_1}^2 = \vec{v}_{f_1}^2 + 2\vec{v}_{f_1}\vec{v}_{f_2} + \vec{v}_{f_2}^2$ $\underline{\vec{v}_{i_1}^2 = \vec{v}_{f_1}^2 + \vec{v}_{f_2}^2}$ $0 = 2\vec{v}_{f_1}\vec{v}_{f_2}$	
6	$\vec{v}_{f_2} > 0$, so $\vec{v}_{f_1} = 0$	
7		$\vec{v}_{i_1} = \vec{v}_{f_1} + \vec{v}_{f_2}$ $\quad = 0 + \vec{v}_{f_2}$ $\vec{v}_{i_1} = \vec{v}_{f_2}$
8	After the collision, the cue ball stops and the other ball shoots forwards with the initial velocity of the cue ball.	

Head-on Elastic Collisions

Textbook pp. 240–248

> **Vocabulary**
>
> head-on elastic collision

MAIN IDEA: In a perfectly elastic head-on collision in one dimension, momentum and kinetic energy are conserved.

1. Define a head-on collision. K/U

2. Define a perfectly elastic collision. K/U

3. Give an example of a head-on collision that is not perfectly elastic. A

MAIN IDEA: The final velocities of two objects in a perfectly elastic head-on collision in one dimension can be determined using the following equations:

$$\vec{v}_{f_1} = \left[\frac{m_1 - m_2}{m_1 + m_2}\right]\vec{v}_{i_1} + \left[\frac{2m_2}{m_1 + m_2}\right]\vec{v}_{i_2} \text{ and } \vec{v}_{f_2} = \left[\frac{m_2 - m_1}{m_1 + m_2}\right]\vec{v}_{i_2} + \left[\frac{2m_1}{m_1 + m_2}\right]\vec{v}_{i_1}$$

4. Indicate whether the following statements are true or false. If you think the statement is false, rewrite it to make it true. K/U T/I

   (a) When two or more objects collide, the change in velocity of one object is equal in magnitude to that of the other object.

   (b) Two colliding objects will only experience the same velocity change if they have the same mass, and the collision occurs in an isolated system.

5. Describe each part of the final velocity equation in words. K/U C

   (a) $\vec{v}_{f_1} = \left[\dfrac{m_1 - m_2}{m_1 + m_2}\right]\vec{v}_{i_1} + \left[\dfrac{2m_2}{m_1 + m_2}\right]\vec{v}_{i_2}$

> **STUDY TIP**
>
> **Variables and Expressions**
> Think about what each variable and expression in an equation represents, so that you understand the meaning, not just the form, of the equation.

(b) $\vec{v}_{f_1} = \left[\dfrac{m_1 - m_2}{m_1 + m_2} \right] \vec{v}_{i_1} + \left[\dfrac{2m_2}{m_1 + m_2} \right] \vec{v}_{i_2}$

6. In cases where $\vec{v}_{i_2}$ is initially zero, $\vec{v}_{f_1} = \left[\dfrac{m_1 - m_2}{m_1 + m_2} \right] \vec{v}_{i_1}$ and $\vec{v}_{f_2} = \left[\dfrac{2m_1}{m_1 + m_2} \right] \vec{v}_{i_1}$. Explain why. K/U C

7. Two balls collide in a head-on elastic collision. The mass of ball 1 is 2.50 kg and its initial velocity is 10.0 m/s [N]. The mass of ball 2 is 1.50 kg and its initial velocity is 7.0 m/s [S]. Calculate the velocity of ball 1 immediately after the collision. T/I

MAIN IDEA: In cases where the masses of the colliding objects are identical, $\vec{v}_{f_1} = \vec{v}_{i_2}$ and $\vec{v}_{f_2} = \vec{v}_{i_1}$. In cases in which one mass is significantly larger than the other mass, and the larger mass is stationary, $\vec{v}_{f_1} \approx -\vec{v}_{i_1}$ and $\vec{v}_{f_2} \approx 0$.

8. Two balls of identical mass collide in a head-on elastic collision. The initial velocity of ball 1 is 8.0 m/s [E]. What is the final velocity of ball 2 immediately after the collision? T/I

9. A marble collides head on with a textbook that is lying on the floor. Describe the magnitude and the direction of the final velocities of the marble and textbook. T/I

MAIN IDEA: During a head-on collision in one dimension, the kinetic energy of the moving masses is converted into elastic potential energy, and then back into kinetic energy during the rebound. Total mechanical energy is conserved throughout the collision.

10. Two curling stones collide head on. Describe the energy transformations that occur during the compression and the rebound. K/U C

11. The graph in **Figure 1** shows what happens to the total kinetic, elastic, and mechanical energy of a system in a head-on elastic collision. Complete the labels with the terms *kinetic, elastic,* and *mechanical.* K/U C

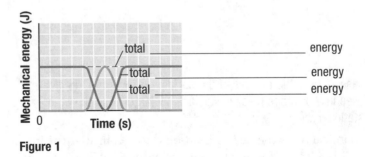

total _____ energy

total _____ energy

total _____ energy

Figure 1

12. Two carts collide. One of the carts has a spring bumper. If the compression of the spring bumper during the collision is x, then the law of conservation of energy states: K/U

$$\frac{1}{2}m_1\vec{v}_{i_1}^2 + \frac{1}{2}m_2\vec{v}_{i_2}^2 = \frac{1}{2}m_1\vec{v}_{f_1}^2 + \frac{1}{2}m_2\vec{v}_{f_2}^2 + \frac{1}{2}kx^2$$

(a) What does k represent is this equation? _____

(b) What does x represent is this equation? _____

13. At maximum compression, two colliding objects connected by a spring must have the same velocity, v_f. Complete the equation below to represent the situation during maximum compression: **K/U**

$$\frac{1}{2}m_1\vec{v}_{i_1}^2 + \frac{1}{2}m_2\vec{v}_{i_2}^2 = \qquad + \frac{1}{2}kx^2$$

14. Two carts travel toward one another on a track. Each cart has a mass of 25 kg. Cart 1 is moving at 20 m/s [right] and cart 2 is moving left at twice the speed. The carts collide in a head-on elastic collision cushioned by a spring with spring constant 6.5×10^5 N/m. At the point of maximum compression of the spring, the carts both have the same velocity, v_f. **T/I**

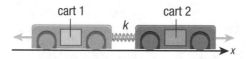

(a) What will be the velocity of each cart as the carts separate? Explain.

(b) Determine the maximum compression of the spring.

Collisions in Two Dimensions: Glancing Collisions

Textbook pp. 249–253

> **Vocabulary**
>
> glancing collision

MAIN IDEA: The laws of conservation of momentum and conservation of kinetic energy for collisions in two dimensions are the same as for one-dimensional collisions.

1. Describe how an object travels in a glancing collision after it collides with another object. K/U C

2. Write the conservation of momentum equation in terms of horizontal components. K/U

$$\vec{p}\rule{1cm}{0.4pt} + \vec{p}\rule{1cm}{0.4pt} = \vec{p}\rule{1cm}{0.4pt} + \vec{p}\rule{1cm}{0.4pt}$$

3. Two hockey pucks of mass 0.20 kg collide. Initially, puck 1 moved at 35 m/s to the right and puck 2 was at rest. After the collision, puck 1 moves at 20.0 m/s at an angle of $\theta = 45°$ from the original direction of motion. What is the velocity of puck 2 after the collision? Complete the solution. T/I

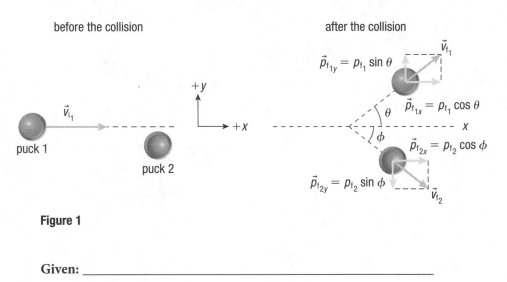

before the collision   after the collision

Figure 1

Given: _____

Required: _____

Analysis: Determine the total vector momentum before and after the collision. Use components of vectors to determine the momentum of puck 2 after the collision. Then, determine the velocity of puck 2 after the collision.

Solution:

(a) Use **Table 1** and **Table 2** to calculate the total momentum before and after the collision.

Table 1 Total Momentum Before the Collision

	In the x-direction	In the y-direction
puck 1	$\vec{p} = m\vec{v}$ $=$ $=$	$\vec{p} = m\vec{v}$ $= 0$
puck 2	$\vec{p} = m\vec{v}$ $=$	$\vec{p} = m\vec{v}$ $=$
Total	$\vec{p} =$	$\vec{p} =$

Table 2 Total Momentum After the Collision

	In the x-direction	In the y-direction
puck 1	$\vec{p} = m\vec{v}\cos\theta$ $=$ $=$	$\vec{p} = m\vec{v}\sin\theta$ $=$ $=$
puck 2	$\vec{p} = m\vec{v}\cos\phi$ $=$	$\vec{p} = m\vec{v}\sin\phi$ $=$
Total	$\vec{p} =$	$\vec{p} =$

(b) Use **Table 3** to calculate the components of the velocity.

Table 3 Components of the Velocity

In the x-direction ($\vec{v}_x$)	In the y-direction ($\vec{v}_y$)
_____ kg·m/s + (_____ kg)$\vec{v}\cos\phi =$ _____ kg·m/s $=$ $=$ $=$ $=$	_____ kg·m/s + (_____ kg)$\vec{v}\sin\phi =$ _____ kg·m/s $=$ $=$ $=$

(c) Calculate the magnitude of the velocity.

$$\vec{v}_2^{\,2} = \vec{v}_x^{\,2} + \vec{v}_y^{\,2}$$

(d) Determine the direction.

$$\tan\phi = \frac{\vec{v}_y}{\vec{v}_x}$$

Statement: The velocity of puck 2 is _____.

Explore Applications of Momentum

Textbook pp. 254–255

Staying Safe at Every Speed

MAIN IDEA: Scientists and engineers design safety devices by analyzing the transfer of energy and momentum in collisions.

1. Use **Table 1** to list some motor vehicle safety devices and their purposes. K/U C

Table 1 Motor Vehicle Safety Devices

Safety device	Purpose

2. Summarize information about a motor vehicle safety device (other than seat belts) by filling in the fishbone diagram below. K/U C A

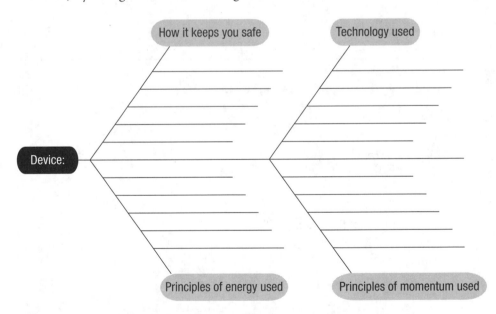

3. Based on the information you recorded above, would you recommend this motor vehicle safety device to a friend? Explain your response. T/I A

Physics JOURNAL

Momentum and the Neutrino

Textbook pp. 256–257

MAIN IDEA: Neutrinos were predicted as a way to account for missing energy and momentum in beta decay, a type of radioactive decay of atomic nuclei.

1. Complete the statements. K/U

   Neutrinos are produced in nuclear reactions in _____ and
   _____. There are three types of neutrinos: _____ neutrinos,
   _____ neutrinos, and _____ neutrinos. A neutrino of one
   type can _____ into either of the other two types and back again.
   _____ of neutrinos pass through each square centimetre of Earth's
   surface each second.

2. (a) Which scientist first predicted the existence of the neutrino?

   _____

   (b) What did he originally call his new particle? _____

   (c) Who developed the idea of a missing particle into a full theory of
       beta decay? _____ K/U

3. The Sudbury Neutrino Observatory detector is located 2 km underground near
   Sudbury, Ontario. Why was it built far underground? K/U

4. What other method was used by the Sudbury Neutrino Observatory detector
   to increase the likelihood of neutrino interaction? K/U

5. What is the IceCube Neutrino Observatory experiment? K/U

Momentum and Collisions

Use the graphic organizer below to summarize what you have learned about work, energy, and periodic motion. You can add your own notes, diagrams, and equations to this graphic organizer, creating a study tool to help you review Chapter 5.

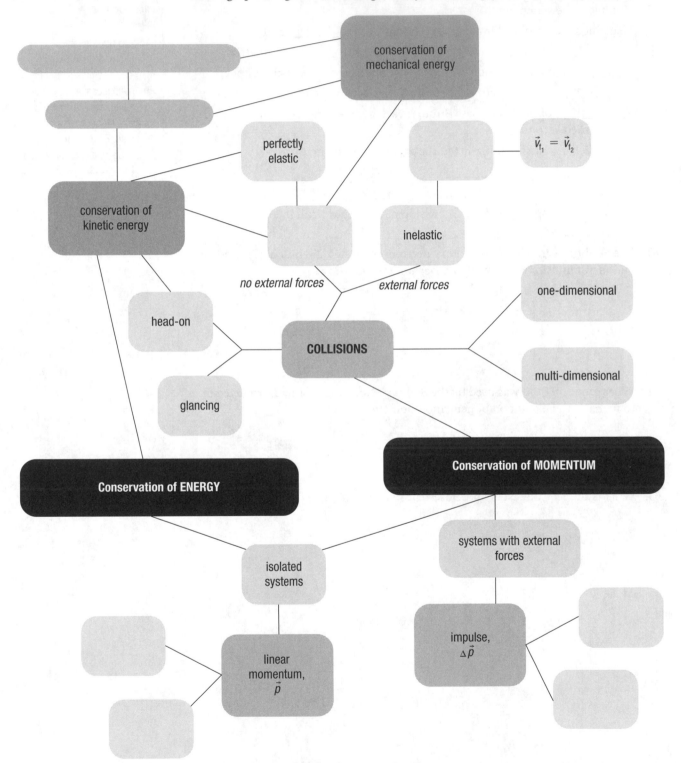

1. Indicate whether each statement is true or false. If you think the statement is false, rewrite it to make it true. (5.1, 5.2, 5.3) K/U

   K/U   Knowledge/Understanding
   T/I   Thinking/Investigation
   C   Communication
   A   Application

   (a) In the absence of an external force, an object with constant mass must also have constant linear momentum.

   (b) A compact car and a large truck have a head-on collision. The momentum transferred from the truck to the car is greater than and in the same directions as the momentum transferred from the car to the truck.

   (c) A ball is dropped from rest, and collides with the ground. The higher the ball rises upon collision with the ground, the more elastic the collision is.

2. In the space below, create a Venn diagram that compares conservation of momentum and conservation of kinetic energy. (5.2, 5.3) K/U C

3. A baseball of mass 0.15 kg is pitched at 35 m/s [forwards] at a batter. The ball knocks the stationary 0.85 kg bat out of the batter's hands, and the ball rebounds at 24 m/s [backwards]. (5.1, 5.2, 5.3) K/U T/I

   (a) What is the initial momentum of the ball?

(b) What is the ball's momentum just after it hits the bat?

(c) How much momentum is transferred to the bat?

(d) Calculate the velocity of the bat as it leaves the batter.

(e) Calculate the kinetic energy before and after the collision of bat and ball. Is the collision elastic or inelastic?

4. If an object has momentum, must it also have mechanical energy? Explain. (5.4) K/U

5. In one-dimensional collisions,
    (a) kinetic energy is conserved if the collision is elastic
    (b) momentum is conserved in the x-direction
    (c) momentum is conserved in the y-direction
    (d) All of the above are true. (5.5) K/U
6. In two-dimensional collisions,
    (a) kinetic energy is conserved if the collision is elastic
    (b) momentum is conserved in the x-direction
    (c) momentum is conserved in the y-direction
    (d) All of the above are true. (5.5) K/U

1. According to the work-energy theorem, what is equal to the total work done on an object? (4.2) K/U
   (a) the object's potential energy
   (b) the change in the object's potential energy
   (c) the object's kinetic energy
   (d) the change in the object's total energy

2. What is the momentum of a bowling ball with a mass of 6.0 kg travelling at 4.0 m/s? (5.2) K/U A
   (a) 0.67 kg·m/s   (b) 1.5 kg·m/s   (c) 24 kg·m/s   (d) 48 kg·m/s

3. In which type of collision is an idealized situation where momentum and kinetic energy are completely conserved? (5.3) K/U
   (a) elastic collision   (c) inelastic collision
   (b) perfectly elastic collision   (d) perfectly inelastic collision

4. Indicate whether each statement is true or false. If you think the statement is false, rewrite it to make it true. K/U
   (a) Energy is always conserved in an open system. (4.6)

   (b) Hooke's law states that the force exerted by a spring is indirectly proportional to the spring's displacement from its rest equilibrium position. (4.6)

   (c) A glancing collision between two objects results both objects travelling at an angle to the direction of their original courses. (5.3)

5. A crate is pushed 3.6 m with a constant force of 62 N in the same direction as its motion. Calculate the amount of work done on the crate if the angle between the applied force and the displacement of the crate is 15°. (4.1) T/I A

6. A crane lifts a steel I-beam 75 m. The lift increases the gravitational potential energy of the I-beam by 2.6×10^5 J. Determine the mass of the I-beam. (4.3) T/I A

K/U Knowledge/Understanding
T/I Thinking/Investigation
C   Communication
A   Application

7. (a) After hanging a 1.6 kg mass from a spring, the spring stretches 78 cm from its equilibrium position. Determine the spring constant.

(b) Determine the elastic potential energy of this spring when two 1.6 kg masses are hung from it. (4.6) T/I A

8. A 57 g tennis ball is at rest at its maximum height during a serve. The player then hits it and exerts an average horizontal force of magnitude 1.8 N on the ball. Determine the speed of the ball after the player hits it if the average force is exerted on the ball for 0.45 s. (5.1) T/I A

9. While at rest during a spacewalk, an astronaut is 12 m from an entrance to the space station. To reach the entrance, she faces away from the entrance and throws a 0.50 kg wrench directly in front of her at a speed of 25 m/s. Determine how long will it take her to travel the 12 m if the astronaut and her spacesuit have a combined mass of 115 kg. (5.2) T/I

10. A curling stone travelling at 2.1 m/s collides with an identical curling stone at rest. After the collision, the stones have the same speed, and are moving at an angle of 29° from the original direction of motion of the thrown stone, one to the left, and the other to the right. Determine the final velocity of the thrown stone. (5.5) T/I C A

Gravitational, Electric, and Magnetic Fields

Chapter 6: Gravitational Fields

The universal law of gravitation states that the force of gravitational attraction between any two objects is directly proportional to the product of the masses and inversely proportional to the square of the distance between their centres.

The gravitational field can be represented by a vector at each point in space and it exerts forces on objects with mass.

The speed of a satellite in uniform circular motion around a central body depends on the mass of the body and the radius of the orbit. For a given orbital radius, a satellite in a circular orbit has a constant speed.

Chapter 7: Electric Fields

Electric charges are either positive or negative. Objects that have an equal number of positive and negative charges are neutral. Electrons are the only subatomic particles capable of being transferred from one object to another. Unlike charges attract each other; like charges repel each other. The total charge of a closed system remains constant.

The force between two point charges is directly proportional to the product of the charges and inversely proportional to the square of the distance between the charges. This is known as Coulomb's Law. The superposition principle states that the total force acting on a charge is the vector sum of the individual forces exerted on the charge by all the other charges in the system.

An electric field of force exists in a region of space when a test charge placed at any point in the region has a force exerted upon it. Electric field lines are continuous lines of force around a charge or charges. An electric dipole consists of two equal but opposite charges separated by a small distance. The electric field between two parallel charged plates is uniform and perpendicular to the plates.

The change in electric potential energy depends on the electric field, the charge being moved, and the displacement of the charge. The electric potential is the electric potential energy per unit charge at a given point. The total electric potential at a point P for a system of charges equals the algebraic sum of the potentials at P due to each individual charge. The Millikan oil drop experiment established the existence of a fundamental unit of charge equal to the charge on the proton.

Chapter 8: Magnetic Fields

All magnets have magnetic poles. Opposite poles attract while like poles repel. A magnetic field surrounds all magnets and is directed from north to south outside the magnet, and south to north inside the magnet. Moving electric charges produce a magnetic field.

A charge moving in a magnetic field experiences a force. The force depends on the velocity of the particle, the magnetic field, and the angle between them. A right-hand rule determines the direction of the force, which is perpendicular to both the velocity of the charge and the direction of the magnetic field.

A current-carrying wire in a magnetic field experiences a force if the wire is not parallel to the field lines. A charged particle moving perpendicular to a magnetic field follows a circular path. If the velocity is neither perpendicular nor parallel to the field, the particle follows a spiral path along the field lines.

Electric and magnetic fields find applications in radio-frequency identification technology, magnetorheological fluids, and magnetic resonance imaging.

BIG IDEAS

- Gravitational, electric, and magnetic forces act on matter from a distance.

- Gravitational, electric, and magnetic fields share many similar properties.

- The behaviour of matter in gravitational, electric, and magnetic fields can be described mathematically.

- Technological systems that involve gravitational, electric, and magnetic fields can have an effect on society and the environment.

Newtonian Gravitation

Textbook pp. 288–296

> **Vocabulary**
>
> gravitational constant (G)   gravitational field
>
> inverse-square law   gravitational field strength

MAIN IDEA: The force of gravitational attraction between an object with mass m_1, another object of mass m_2, and a distance between their centres, r, is represented by the equation $F_g = \dfrac{Gm_1m_2}{r^2}$, where G is an empirical constant called the gravitational constant.

1. Indicate whether each of the following statements is true or false. If you think the statement is false, rewrite it to make it true. K/U

   (a) Your fingernail exerts a gravitational pull on the Sun.

   (b) The magnitude of the gravitational force exerted by Earth on you equals the magnitude of the gravitational force exerted by you on Earth.

   (c) The gravitational force exerted by a tree on you is directly dependent upon the distance between you and the tree.

   (d) The gravitational force exerted by you on a bird decreases as the bird flies away.

> **LEARNING TIP**
>
> **Action and Reaction**
> Gravitational forces are action–reaction pairs. These terms suggest that the two forces are different in some way. Actually, they are simply two forces that occur together at an instant of time and act on different objects.

2. (a) Complete **Table 1** to show the effect of mass on the gravitational force. K/U C

   Table 1 Effect of Mass on the Gravitational Force

Mass of object 1 (kg)	Mass of object 2 (kg)	Distance between objects (m)	Force of attraction between objects (N)
1	1	r	F_g
1	2	r	$2F_g$
2		r	$4F_g$
1	3	r	
2	$\dfrac{1}{2}$	r	

(b) Complete **Table 2** to show the effect of distance on the gravitational force.

K/U C

Table 2 Effect of Distance on the Gravitational Force

Mass of object 1 (kg)	Mass of object 2 (kg)	Distance between objects (m)	Force of attraction between objects (N)
m	m	r	F_g
m	m	$2r$	$\frac{1}{4}F_g$
m	m	$3r$	
m	m	$\frac{1}{2}r$	
m	m		$25F_g$

MAIN IDEA: The gravitational constant is $G = 6.67 \times 10^{-11}$ N·m²/kg².

3. A proton with a mass of 1.7×10^{-27} kg is located 1.0×10^4 km above the surface of Earth. Earth's mass and radius are approximately 6.0×10^{24} kg and 6.4×10^6 m, respectively. T/I

   (a) How far is the centre of the proton from the centre of Earth?

   (b) What is the magnitude of the gravitational force between Earth and the proton?

STUDY TIP

Calculations
When reviewing equations used for calculations, be sure to note the units from the variables in the equation.

4. At what distance apart would two equal masses of 175 kg need to be placed for the gravitational force between them to be 3.0×10^{-5} N? T/I

5. Earth, the Moon, and the Sun are aligned during a lunar eclipse (**Figure 1**).
   The Moon has a mass of 7.35×10^{22} kg and is 3.8×10^8 m from Earth. Earth
   has a mass of 5.98×10^{24} kg and is 1.5×10^{11} m from the Sun. The Sun has a
   mass of 1.99×10^{30} kg. Calculate the net gravitational force exerted by both
   the Moon and Sun on Earth. T/I

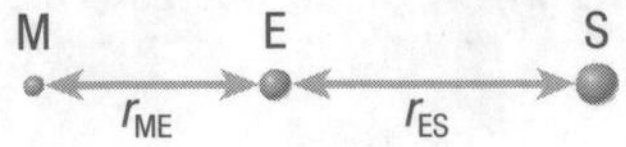

M   E   S

r_{ME} r_{ES}

Figure 1

MAIN IDEA: The gravitational field strength at a distance r from a body of mass m equals
the magnitude of gravitational acceleration at that distance: $g = \dfrac{Gm}{r^2}$.

6. (a) What is a gravitational field?

   (b) Draw a diagram to represent Earth's gravitational field. K/U C

7. The magnitude of the strength of a gravitational field is _____ the magnitude of the acceleration of objects under its influence. K/U

8. What is the approximate gravitational field strength, g, on Earth? K/U
   (a) 9.8 m/s
   (b) 9.8 N
   (c) 9.8 N/kg
   (d) 9.8 N·m²/kg²

9. What happens to the acceleration due to gravity, g, as an object moves away from Earth's surface? K/U
   (a) It increases.
   (b) It stays the same.
   (c) It varies slightly.
   (d) It decreases.

10. (a) Calculate the magnitude of the gravitational acceleration of an object on the surface of Mars. Assume Mars is a perfect sphere, with a mass of 6.42×10^{23} kg and a radius of 3.40×10^{6} m.

    (b) The gravitational acceleration on Earth is approximately 9.8 m/s². Approximately how many times less would a cat's weight be on Mars than on Earth? T/I

Orbits

Textbook pp. 297–303

Vocabulary

satellite

artificial satellite

space station

orbital radius

geosynchronous orbit

MAIN IDEA: Satellites can be natural, such as moons around planets, or artificial, such as the RADARSAT satellites and the International Space Station.

1. Complete the Venn diagram to explain how natural and artificial satellites are the same and different. K/U C

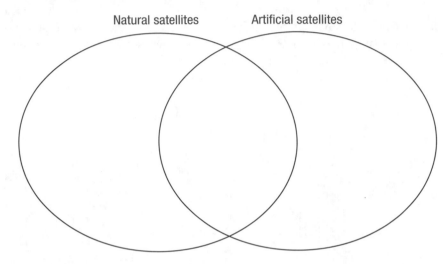

Natural satellites   Artificial satellites

2. The International Space Station allows scientists to study human responses to microgravity. What is a microgravity environment? Give a different example of a situation in which a person is experiencing microgravity. K/U A

MAIN IDEA: The speed, v, of a satellite in uniform circular motion around a central body depends on the mass of the central body, m, and the radius of the orbit, r: $v = \sqrt{\dfrac{Gm}{r}}$.

3. What does the equation $v = \sqrt{\dfrac{Gm}{r}}$ tell us about the relationship between the speed of a satellite and its mass? K/U T/I

4. The distance between the centre of a satellite and the centre of its parent body is called the _____. K/U

5. For a satellite to maintain an orbit of radius r, its speed must be _____. K/U

6. Indicate whether each of the following statements is true or false. If the statement is false, rewrite it to make it true. K/U

   (a) The orbital speed of a geosynchronous orbit matches the rate of Earth's rotation.

   (b) The period of a geosynchronous orbit is exactly one Earth day.

   (c) In a geostationary orbit, the satellite does not orbit directly above the equator.

   (d) A geostationary satellite appears to travel through the same point in the sky every 24 h.

7. Earth orbits the Sun at an average distance of about 150 million kilometres every 365.26 solar days. T/I

   (a) What is Earth's average orbital speed in km/s?

   (b) What is the Sun's mass?

STUDY TIP

Highlighting Key Points
As you read through the Study Guide, underline or highlight the answers that summarize points in the chapter that you want to review in the textbook or discuss with others.

Explore Applications of Gravitational Fields

Satellites

MAIN IDEA: Satellite applications range from Earth imaging to climate change research, and from weather tracking and naval support to search and rescue, media broadcasting, and other scientific studies. Satellites are crucial for our navigation, and communication systems. They also have military applications.

1. Complete the organizer below to describe an application of satellites. C A

Type of Satellite

Purpose	Sketch
How the satellite uses Earth's gravitational field to obtain the desired orbit	How the satellite collects, uses, or shares data
Research findings	Questions raised

2. In what ways does the satellite's operation affect society and the environment? T/I A

Physics JOURNAL

General Relativity

Textbook pp. 306–307

MAIN IDEA: Einstein's theory of general relativity explains gravity in terms of the geometry of space and time.

1. What was Einstein's breakthrough idea that led to the theory of general relativity? K/U

2. In Newton's theory of gravity, a change in the position of a mass in one part of the universe instantly changes its gravitational field in all other parts of the universe. How does the theory of general relativity differ? K/U

3. Newton's theory of gravity predicts that since light does not have mass, it experiences and exerts no force. How does general relativity differ? K/U

> ### STUDY TIP
>
> **Asking Questions**
> Questions about a reading passage can be used to help you understand the main ideas. After you complete a reading, ask yourself or a partner questions about the main ideas of your reading. Use your answers to reinforce what you have read.

4. In Newton's theory, the pair of stars in a binary system would circle each other with no changes. What does general relativity say will happen? K/U

5. Do all objects in the universe behave in the way general relativity predicts? Explain. K/U

6. (a) What is a black hole?

   (b) How are black holes detected? K/U

7. What is dark matter? K/U

Gravitational Fields

Use the graphic organizer below to summarize what you have learned about gravitational fields. You can add your own notes, diagrams, and equations to this graphic organizer, creating a study tool to help you review Chapter 6.

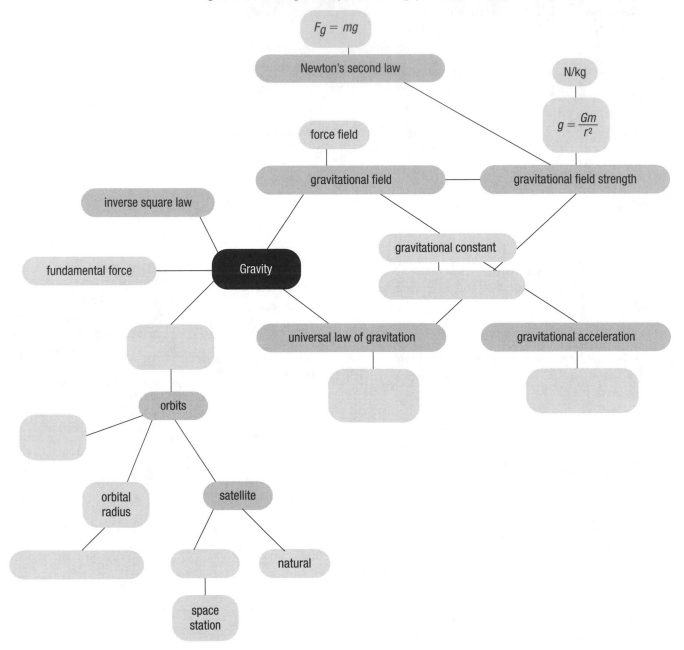

1. Match each term or variable on the left with the correct statement on the right. (6.1, 6.2) K/U

(a) satellite	(i) decreases with increasing height above Earth's surface
(b) microgravity	
(c) g	(ii) appears in the universal law of gravitation
(d) gravitational constant	(iii) revolves around another body due to gravitational attraction
(e) v	
(f) inverse-square law	(iv) must be constant for a satellite to maintain an orbit of radius r
(g) gravitational field strength	
	(v) the universal law of gravitation follows this
	(vi) magnitude of the gravitational field vector at a point in space
	(vii) present when any object is in free fall

2. Indicate whether each statement is true or false. If you think the statement is false, rewrite it to make it true. K/U

   (a) The mass of a satellite determines its orbital speed. (6.2)

   (b) A satellite in geosynchronous orbit has a constant orbital radius. (6.2)

3. The magnitude of the gravitational force of attraction between two objects of equal mass is 5.0×10^3 N. The objects are 5.0 m apart. What is the mass of each object? (6.1) T/I

4. What happens to the magnitude of the gravitational field strength under each condition? (6.1) K/U

   (a) r decreases by a factor of 4

   (b) m doubles

5. Calculate the magnitude of the gravitational force exerted by the Moon on a 75 kg astronaut standing on the Moon. The Moon has a mass of 7.35×10^{22} kg, and its radius is 1.74×10^6 m. (6.1) T/I

6. An astronaut is in orbit 3.5×10^4 km from Earth's centre. Earth's mass is approximately 5.98×10^{24} kg. Determine the magnitude of the gravitational field strength at the location of the astronaut. (6.1) [T/I]

7. Titan orbits Saturn with an orbital radius of 1.2×10^6 km. Saturn's mass is approximately 5.69×10^{26} kg. (6.2) [T/I]
   (a) Calculate Titan's orbital speed.

   (b) Calculate Titan's orbital period.

8. Einstein developed and shaped theories through "What if?"–style mental exercises called *thought experiments*. Create your own thought experiment on the subject of gravity. Remember, special relativity has not answered all the questions about our universe, and as Einstein said, "Imagination is more important than knowledge." (6.4) [T/I] [C]

Properties of Electric Charge

Vocabulary			
coulomb (C)	conductor	insulator	

Textbook pp. 320–326

MAIN IDEA: Electric charges are either positive or negative. Objects may be positive, negative, or neutral depending on the charge balance. Electrons are the only subatomic particles capable of being transferred from one object to another. Protons are bound to the atomic nucleus.

1. An atom becomes a cation by _____. Explain your answer. K/U T/I
   (a) gaining protons
   (b) losing electrons
   (c) losing protons
   (d) either (a) or (b)

2. How many electrons are needed to make up one coulomb of charge? T/I

3. The charge on a party balloon that has been rubbed against fabric is about 1 μC. How many electrons are transferred in charging the balloon? T/I A

4. Which statement is true of conductors of electricity? K/U
   (a) They are always metals.
   (b) They contain electrons that can move freely through the conductor.
   (c) They must always contain some copper.
   (d) all of the above

> ### LEARNING **TIP**
>
> **Attraction and Repulsion**
> The terms "negative" and "positive" were used by Benjamin Franklin to describe the two kinds of electricity that he observed. At the time, atomic theory was still in the future and no one had any knowledge of atomic structure or subatomic particles. Attraction can occur between two bodies with opposite charges, but also between a charged body and a neutral body. Repulsion only occurs between two bodies with like charges.

MAIN IDEA: Unlike electric charges attract each other. Like electric charges repel each other. Charge can be created or destroyed, but the total charge of a closed system remains constant. Objects can be charged by friction, by induced charge separation, by contact, and by induction.

5. A glass rod is rubbed with fur and becomes positively charged. What is the result of this action? Explain your answer. K/U

   (a) The charge will stay where the rod was rubbed with the fur.

   (b) The charge will move throughout the rod until it is evenly distributed.

   (c) The rod will remain charged forever, unless touched with another charged object.

   (d) The charge will be neutralized after a short time by free electrons in the glass.

6. Refer to **Table 1** for the electrostatic series. What is the result if a carbon rod is rubbed with wool? Explain your answer. K/U

   Table 1 Electrostatic Series

	weak hold on electrons
acetate	
glass	
wool	
cat fur, human hair	
calcium, lead	
silk	increasing tendency to gain electrons
aluminum	
cotton	
paraffin wax	
ebonite	
polyethylene (plastic)	
carbon, copper, nickel	
sulfur	
platinum, gold	strong hold on electrons

   (a) Both will remain neutral.

   (b) Both will become negatively charged.

   (c) The carbon will become negatively charged, and the wool will become positively charged.

   (d) The carbon will become positively charged, and the wool will become negatively charged.

7. Is the following statement true or false? If you think the statement is false, rewrite it to make it true: Electrical appliances are grounded to protect users from possible electric shock. K/U

8. Charging by induction using a positively charged wand

   (a) results in a negative charge on the target object

   (b) requires access to an electrical ground

   (c) uses Earth as a source of electrons

   (d) all of the above K/U

Coulomb's Law

Textbook pp. 327–333

Vocabulary

electric force (F_E)   Coulomb's constant (k)   superposition principle

MAIN IDEA: According to Coulomb's law, the force between two point charges is directly proportional to the product of the charges, and inversely proportional to the square of the distance between the charges, given as $F_E = \dfrac{kq_1q_2}{r^2}$. Coulomb's constant $k = 8.99 \times 10^9$ Nm^2/C^2. Coulomb's law applies to point charges, and to charges that can be concentrated equivalently in points located at the centre, when the sizes of the charges are much smaller than their distance of separation. There are similarities between the electric force and the gravitational force.

1. Two charged points experience an electric force F between them. The distance between the points is doubled. What is the electric force after the doubling? Explain your answer. K/U T/I

   (a) $\dfrac{1}{4}F$

   (b) $\dfrac{1}{2}F$

   (c) F

   (d) $2F$

> **STUDY TIP**
>
> **Vector Force Problems**
> You can simplify many vector force problems by using symmetry, especially when charges are located on the vertices of a regular polygon such as an equilateral triangle or a square.

2. The electric force and the gravitational force
   (a) can be either attractive or repulsive
   (b) have about the same magnitude over the same distance
   (c) have greatly different magnitudes, with the electric force the weaker of the two
   (d) have greatly different magnitudes with the gravitational force the weaker of the two K/U

3. Two balloons are each given a charge of 2.00 μC, and separated by a distance of 0.500 m between their centres. What is the electric force between the balloons? T/I A

MAIN IDEA: The superposition principle states that the total force acting on a charge q is the vector sum, or superposition, of the individual forces exerted on q by all the other charges in the system.

4. Two point charges Q and $2Q$ are fixed in place and separated by a distance d as shown in **Figure 1**. For what value of x will a small test charge q feel no net force from the two charges? K/U

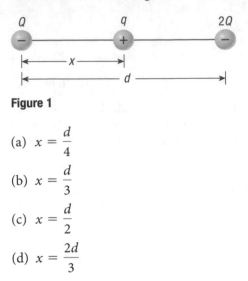

Figure 1

(a) $x = \dfrac{d}{4}$

(b) $x = \dfrac{d}{3}$

(c) $x = \dfrac{d}{2}$

(d) $x = \dfrac{2d}{3}$

5. **Figure 2** shows three point charges of 15.0 μC each are arranged on the vertices of an equilateral triangle of side length 0.400 m. Determine the vector electric force experienced by charge q_1 due to the other two charges. Draw diagrams to help you. T/I C A

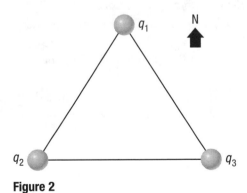

Figure 2

Electric Fields

Vocabulary

electric field ($\vec{\varepsilon}$)   electric field lines   electric dipole

MAIN IDEA: An electric field of force exists in a region of space when a test charge placed at any point in the region has a force exerted upon it. The electric field is a vector denoted by $\vec{\varepsilon}$. A test charge will experience an electric force given by $\vec{F_E} = q\vec{\varepsilon}$. The directions of the electric force and electric field are determined by a positive test charge. For a point charge q_2, the magnitude of the electric field at a distance r from the charge is $\varepsilon = \dfrac{kq_2}{r^2}$. Electric field lines are continuous lines of force that show the direction of electric force at all points in the electric field around a charge or charges.

1. A test charge, q_1 is positive. The electric field points in the _____ direction as the force that the charge experiences. If the text charge is negative, the electric field points in the _____ direction of the force that the charge experiences. K/U

2. The electric field strength at a distance r from a point charge q is ε. A second point charge equal but opposite in sign to q is placed a distance $2r$ from q. What is the electric field strength halfway between the two charges? Explain your answer. K/U T/I

   (a) 0

   (b) $\dfrac{\varepsilon}{2}$

   (c) ε

   (d) 2ε

3. Four charges equal in magnitude of 12.0 μC are placed on the four corners of a square with side length 0.250 m (**Figure 1**). Determine the electric field experienced by a test charge at the centre of the square. Draw a diagram to help you. T/I C A

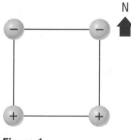

N

Figure 1

Using Diagrams
Use a graphic organizer to illustrate connections among concepts.

MAIN IDEA: An electric dipole consists of two equal but opposite charges separated by some small distance. The electric field between two parallel plates of charge is uniform and perpendicular to the plates. The electric field outside the parallel plates is zero. Applications of electric fields include electrostatic precipitators. Some organisms can detect weak electric fields.

4. Draw arrows on the field lines in **Figure 2** to show the direction of the electric field. K/U

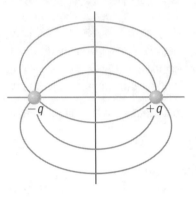

Figure 2

5. The electric field in the atmosphere of Earth
   (a) results from positive ions in the ionosphere
   (b) results from an overall negative charge on Earth's surface
   (c) both (a) and (b)
   (d) is equal to zero K/U

6. List three factors that affect the strength of the electric field between two long parallel plates. K/U

7. Two point charges are arranged as shown in **Figure 3**. The charge on q_1 is 4.5×10^{-6} C while the charge on q_2 is -2.5×10^{-6} C. The distance, r, is 3.5 cm. Calculate the magnitude of the electric field at the origin. T/I

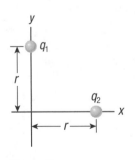

Figure 3

Potential Difference and Electric Potential

Textbook pp. 346–354

Vocabulary

electric potential energy (E_E)   electric potential (V)   electric potential difference (ΔV)

MAIN IDEA: The change in electric potential energy depends on the electric field, the charge being moved, and the charge's displacement: $\Delta E_E = -q\varepsilon\Delta d$. For $\Delta E_E > 0$, work is done against the electric fields ($-W$), resulting in energy stored in the field. For $\Delta E_E < 0$, work is done by the electric field ($+W$) on a particle moving in the field, which typically increases the kinetic energy of the particle.

1. In a particle accelerator, _____ becomes _____. K/U
   (a) electric potential energy, kinetic energy
   (b) kinetic energy, electric potential energy
   (c) electric potential energy, gravitational potential energy
   (d) gravitational potential energy, kinetic energy

2. The electron gun in a cathode ray tube television is 10.0 cm long and creates an electric field of 150 N/C. An electron is accelerated through this field. What is the potential energy difference across the electron gun? T/I A

> **LEARNING TIP**
>
> **Electric Potential**
> Electric potential, or voltage, is sometimes described in elementary science or technical courses as an "electrical pressure". This concept is only useful when modelling electricity using water flow. Voltage is a measure of electrical energy per unit charge, not of force or pressure.

3. A linear accelerator accelerates electrons from rest to 10.0 % of the speed of light across a distance of 1.80 m. What is the average electric field in the accelerator? T/I A

MAIN IDEA: The electric potential is the electric potential energy per unit charge at a given point in the electric field: $V = \dfrac{E_E}{q}$. The magnitude of an electric field varies with the electric potential difference and the change in position in the field: $\varepsilon = \dfrac{\Delta V}{\Delta d}$.

4. Which statement is true of the volt? K/U
   (a) It is a measure of force per unit charge.
   (b) It has units of joules per kilogram.
   (c) It was named after Alessandro Volta.
   (d) all of the above

5. What does electrical potential depend on? K/U
   (a) the amount of charge at a particular location in an electric field
   (b) the electric field strength at that location
   (c) the work done in creating the electric field
   (d) all of the above

6. The picture tube for a colour television of the late twentieth-century required a potential difference of about 3.00×10^4 V to operate the picture tube. How fast were electrons moving when they left the electron gun in such a tube? T/I A

7. The potential difference across the terminals of a car battery is 12.0 V. How much work must the alternator do to charge the battery with 2.16×10^5 C of electrons? T/I A

Electric Potential and Electric Potential Energy Due to Point Charges

Textbook pp. 355–361

Vocabulary

electric potential due to a point charge

MAIN IDEA: The electric potential at a distance r from a point charge q is $V = \dfrac{kq}{r}$. The total electric potential at a point P for a system of charges equals the algebraic sum of the potentials at P due to each individual charge at a distance that separates the charge and P.

1. A point charge q is at the origin, and another point charge $2q$ is a distance d from the origin. Where along the line segment joining the charges is the potential equal to zero? Explain your answer. K/U A

   (a) at $\dfrac{d}{4}$ from the origin

   (b) at $\dfrac{d}{3}$ from the origin

   (c) at $\dfrac{d}{2}$ from the origin

   (d) nowhere along this line segment

2. Charges of 3.00 μC are placed on three corners of a square with side length 0.800 m. What is the potential at the fourth corner of the square? T/I A

> **STUDY TIP**
>
> **Drawing Diagrams**
> Draw diagrams to help you understand the information you are given. Use the diagrams from similar problems and modify them according to the given information.

MAIN IDEA: For an electric potential from a point source charge q_1, the work done moving a test charge q_2 from an initial separation r_i to a final separation r_f equals the change in the electric potential energy. For a system of two charges q_1 and q_2 separated by a distance r, the electric potential energy is $E_E = \dfrac{kq_1q_2}{r}$. The potential energy difference of two point charges q_1 and q_2 as the separation between them changes from r_i to r_f is

$$\Delta E_E = \dfrac{kq_1q_2}{r_f} - \dfrac{kq_1q_2}{r_i}.$$

3. A point charge Q is located at the origin, and another point charge Q is located a distance d along the x-axis. A test charge q is moved from $(0, \dfrac{d}{2})$ on the y-axis to a point halfway between the two charges on the x-axis. Under what condition is the least amount of work done? K/U

   (a) Move q directly from start to finish along a straight line.

   (b) Move q such that it is always perpendicular to the electric field lines.

   (c) Move q along a circular path centred on the origin.

   (d) All of the above require the same amount of work.

4. A proton and an electron are separated by a distance of 1.00×10^{-10} m. Determine the potential energy of the pair of particles. T/I A

5. Point charge q_1 has a charge of 2.5×10^{-6} C, and point charge q_2 has a charge of 9.1×10^{-6} C. Point charge q_1 is initially at rest and 0.30 m from q_2. Point charge q_2 has a mass of 3.8×10^{-9} kg. Both charges are positive with q_1 remaining fixed at the origin while q_2 travels to the right after being released. Determine the speed of charge q_2 when it reaches a distance of 0.45 m from q_2. T/I

6. A proton is accelerated to a speed of 3.00×10^7 m/s and fired at a distant uranium nucleus made up of 92 protons, and 146 neutrons. Assuming that the uranium nucleus remains fixed, how closely will the proton approach the uranium nucleus before coming to a stop? T/I A

The Millikan Oil Drop Experiment

Vocabulary

fundamental physical constant

elementary charge (e)

Textbook pp. 362–365

MAIN IDEA: Robert Millikan used his oil drop experiments to determine the magnitude of an electron's charge. The elementary charge, e, is equal to 1.602×10^{-19} C, and represents the electric charge carried by a proton. The equation $q = Ne$ determines the charge of an object when there are N more protons than electrons.

1. **Figure 1** is a diagram of the Millikan apparatus. Write the labels in their correct positions. K/U

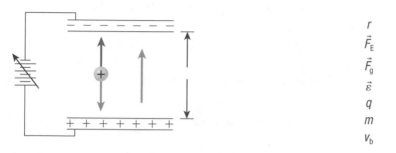

r

$\vec{F}_E$

$\vec{F}_g$

$\vec{\varepsilon}$

q

m

v_b

Figure 1

2. A fundamental physical constant
   (a) depends on location
   (b) is measureable
   (c) cannot be determined by experimentation
   (d) all of the above K/U

3. Calculate the charge on a small sphere with an excess of 4.3×10^{15} electrons. K/U

4. While shuffling her feet across a carpet with socks on, Sarah picked up a negative charge of 120 μC. How many extra electrons did she gain from the carpet? T/I A

5. The Millikan experiment can be performed with latex microspheres, each with a mass of 2.20×10^{-15} kg. What voltage is needed to balance a sphere with an excess charge of 9 electrons between plates that are 3.20 cm apart? T/I A

MAIN IDEA: The value of the charge on an electron is -1.602×10^{-19} C. Every subatomic particle so far detected has a charge whose magnitude is equal to a whole-number multiple of the elementary charge.

6. Which of the following statements about antimatter is true? K/U
   (a) It was predicted by the quantum theory of Dirac.
   (b) It has not yet been verified experimentally.
   (c) It includes protons and electrons.
   (d) It does not have an analogue for a neutron, since a neutron has no electric charge.

7. The electric charge of a proton is equal in magnitude to the absolute value of the electric charge of the electron. Why is this surprising? Explain. T/I

8. Metal plates are placed on the floor and ceiling of a laboratory 3.50 m apart. A balloon has a mass of 1.20×10^{-2} kg. It is inflated and rubbed with fur to give it a charge. When the plates are charged to 8.00×10^4 V, the balloon is balanced. What is the charge on the balloon? T/I A

Electric Fields

Use the graphic organizer below to summarize what you have learned about electric fields. Add lines to connect ideas and concepts. You can add your own notes, diagrams, and equations to this graphic organizer, creating a study tool to help you review Chapter 7.

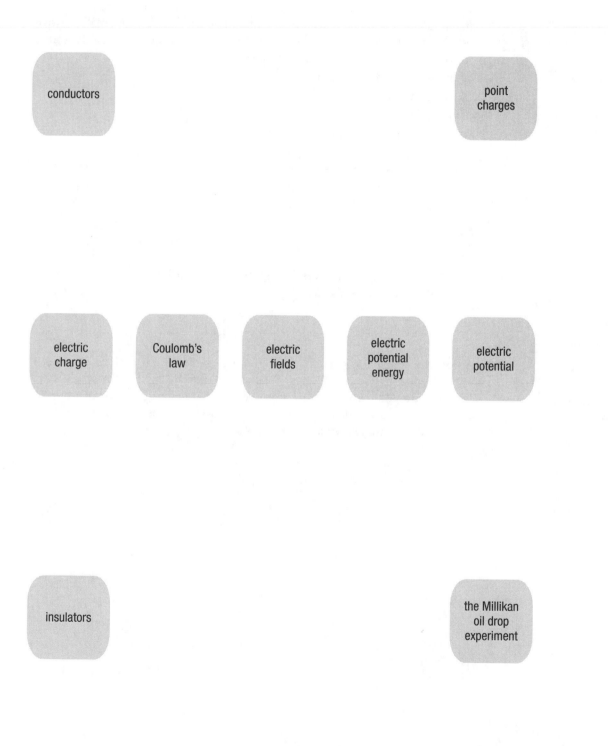

conductors

point charges

electric charge

Coulomb's law

electric fields

electric potential energy

electric potential

insulators

the Millikan oil drop experiment

1. A carbon rod is rubbed with wool. It is found to attract bits of paper. (7.1) **K/U**
   (a) The rod and paper must have opposite charges.
   (b) The rod and paper must have like charges.
   (c) The paper may have an opposite charge or be neutral.
   (d) The paper may have a like charge or be neutral.

2. A positive point charge q is fixed at the origin. A negative point charge of magnitude $3q$ is fixed at a distance d along the positive x-axis. A small positive test charge is placed between them, but closer to the negative charge than the positive charge. The force on this test charge
   (a) points toward the origin
   (b) points toward the positive x-axis
   (c) is equal to zero
   (d) points perpendicular to the x-axis (7.2) **K/U**

3. Indicate whether each statement is true or false. If you think the statement is false, rewrite it to make it true. **K/U**
   (a) An electric field is a region in which a force is exerted on an electric charge. (7.3)

   (b) Electric potential energy is energy stored in an electric field that cannot do work on a charged particle. (7.4)

4. A positive charge Q is fixed to the origin. A negative charge with magnitude $9Q$ is fixed along the positive x-axis a distance d to the right of the origin. Determine a point where a small positive test charge q will experience zero electrical force from the two charges, or show that there is no such point. Draw diagrams to help you. (7.2) **T/I** **C** **A**

5. Four charges equal in magnitude of 20.0 μC are placed on the four corners of a square with side length 0.180 m (**Figure 1**). Determine the electric field at the centre of the square. (7.3) T/I A

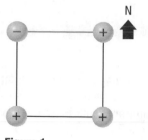

Figure 1

6. An alpha particle has a charge $2e$ and is fixed at the origin. A proton is located 2.00×10^{-8} m from the alpha particle along the positive x-axis. When the proton is released, what is its speed at a great distance from the alpha particle? (7.5) T/I A

7. A water droplet has a mass of 9.84×10^{-15} kg and is suspended between two parallel plates that are 2.24 cm apart. The droplet is charged to 900 V. What is the charge on the droplet measured as elementary charges? (7.6) T/I A

Magnets and Electromagnets

Textbook pp. 378–385

> **Vocabulary**
> magnetic field line

MAIN IDEA: All magnets have magnetic poles. Opposite magnetic poles attract one another and like magnetic poles repel one another. A magnetic field surrounds all magnets, and goes from north to south outside the magnet, and from south to north inside the magnet. Earth's magnetic field resembles that of a bar magnet.

> **LEARNING TIP**
>
> **Magnetic Poles**
> Although we usually call the poles on a magnet "north" and "south," their proper names are "north-seeking pole" and "south-seeking pole." The former names can cause some confusion when working with problems that involve both magnets and geographic directions, such as navigation with a magnetic compass.

1. Which statement about the aurora borealis is true? K/U
   (a) They are produced by cosmic ray protons.
   (b) They result from charged particles spiralling around Earth's magnetic field lines.
   (c) They are more prevalent around the equator.
   (d) all of the above

2. Which statement about magnetic fields is true? K/U
   (a) They are always produced by a magnetic dipole.
   (b) They are considered to flow from a south pole to a north pole outside a magnet.
   (c) They result from static pairs of positive and negative electric charges.
   (d) They attract small bits of paper.

3. Indicate whether each statement is true or false. If you think the statement is false, rewrite it to make it true. K/U
   (a) There are no magnetic field lines inside a magnet.

   (b) The north magnetic pole of Earth is actually the south pole of a magnet.

4. The magnetic poles of Earth
   (a) are always coincident with the geographic poles
   (b) slowly change location over time
   (c) have never reversed their polarity
   (d) allow GPS receivers to determine location K/U

MAIN IDEA: The principle of electromagnetism states that moving electric charges produce a magnetic field. The right-hand rule for a straight conductor states that if your thumb points in the direction of conventional current, your curled fingers indicate the direction of the magnetic field lines around the straight conductor. The right-hand rule for a solenoid states that if the fingers of your right hand curl in the direction of the conventional current, your thumb points in the direction of the magnetic field lines in the centre of the coil.

> **LEARNING TIP**
>
> **Current Direction**
> The direction of conventional current is defined as the direction of flow of positive charge. The direction in which electrons flow (negative charge) in a wire is opposite to the direction of conventional current. When you apply the right-hand rule, consider the direction of conventional current.

5. A wire is placed horizontally, and an electric current flows through the wire from west to east. A magnetic compass needle is held a short distance directly over the wire. The compass needle will point
   (a) south
   (b) north
   (c) east
   (d) in no particular direction T/I A

6. A wire is wound into a coil around a hollow cardboard tube and connected to a battery as shown in **Figure 1**. Which of the following statements describes what will happen? T/I A

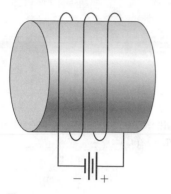

Figure 1

(a) The coil will form a magnet with the north pole at the left.
(b) The coil will form a magnet with the north pole at the right.
(c) The coil will not act as a magnet because cardboard is an insulator.
(d) The coil will only form a magnetic field inside the cardboard tube.

7. In 1820, Hans Christian Oersted demonstrated how a wire becomes warmer when electric charge flows through it. What conclusion did he draw from this experiment? K/U

(a) A magnetic field surrounds moving charges.
(b) Thermal energy is absorbed from the surrounding environment.
(c) Thermal energy is released to the surrounding environment.
(d) all of the above

8. The strength of an electromagnet can be increased by

(a) decreasing the number of turns on the coil
(b) adding an insulating material to the core, such as carbon
(c) increasing the current through the coil
(d) all of the above K/U

9. The strength of an electromagnet can be increased by using a solenoid made of magnetic material. The effect of using the magnetic material for the core is to

(a) decrease the strength of the magnetic field
(b) increase the strength of the magnetic field by aligning electrons with the core material
(c) increase the strength of the magnetic field by creating another electromagnet
(d) all of the above K/U

10. Electromagnets are used rather than permanent magnets for some applications. Why is this? K/U

(a) An electromagnet can be made very strong for a lighter weight.
(b) An electromagnet can be turned on and off.
(c) A powerful electromagnet costs less than a powerful permanent magnet.
(d) all of the above

Magnetic Force on Moving Charges

Textbook pp. 386–391

> **Vocabulary**
>
> tesla

MAIN IDEA: The formula for calculating the magnitude of the magnetic force on a moving charge is $F_M = qvB\sin\theta$, where θ is the angle between $\vec{v}$ and $\vec{B}$.

1. The tesla
   (a) is a unit of magnetic force strength
   (b) is equal to 1 kg/(C·s)
   (c) is used to measure the electric field due to very small charges such as one electron
   (d) was named after the wife of André-Marie Ampère ☒

2. The force acting on a charged particle moving in a magnetic field
   (a) increases as the strength of the field is increased
   (b) decreases with increasing charge
   (c) is parallel to the direction of the field
   (d) all of the above ☒

3. A magnetic field of 1.80 T runs from the ceiling to the floor of the classroom. An electron is shot from south to north at a speed of 5.00×10^6 m/s. Determine the magnitude of the force acting on the electron due to the magnetic field. ☒ ☒

MAIN IDEA: You can use the right-hand rule to determine the direction of the magnetic force on a moving particle. First, point your right thumb in the direction of $\vec{v}$. Then, point your fingers in the direction of $\vec{B}$. If the charge is positive, your palm indicates the direction of a force on the charge. The direction of force is in the opposite direction for a negative charge.

> **STUDY TIP**
>
> **Practice**
> Some concepts are difficult to understand without putting them into practice. For example, practise using the right-hand rule for determining the direction of the magnetic force on a moving particle.

4. Place the labels correctly on **Figure 1** to illustrate the right-hand rule for the force on a moving charge in a magnetic field. ☒ ☒

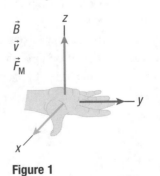

$\vec{B}$
$\vec{v}$
$\vec{F}_M$
z
y
x

Figure 1

5. A magnetic field runs from east to west. A positively charged alpha particle is moving towards the northeast. What is the direction of the magnetic force on the alpha particle? K/U

   (a) up

   (b) down

   (c) southwest

   (d) in no particular direction

6. Describe at least two characteristics of a magnetic force that make it different from gravitational and electric forces. Explain what makes them different. K/U T/I

7. An electron is shot from an electron gun at a speed of 4.45×10^5 m/s from north to south. A magnetic field runs from northeast to southwest. The magnetic force balances the gravitational force on the electron. Determine the strength of the magnetic field. T/I A

Magnetic Force on a Current-Carrying Conductor

Textbook pp. 392–396

MAIN IDEA: The magnetic force on a current-carrying wire is equivalent to the sum of the magnetic forces on all of the moving charges in the wire. A straight, current-carrying conductor in a uniform external magnetic field $\vec{B}$ experiences a magnetic force due to the field. The magnitude of the force is $F_{\text{on wire}} = ILB\sin\theta$, where I is the current in the conductor, L is the length of the conductor, and θ is the angle between the direction of the current and the direction of the magnetic field. The force is greatest when the magnetic field is perpendicular to the current, and zero when the magnetic field is parallel to the current.

1. The force on a current-carrying wire in a magnetic field increases as
   (a) the strength of the current increases
   (b) the length of the wire decreases
   (c) the magnetic field decreases
   (d) all of the above K/U

2. A wire 20.0 cm long carries a current of 24.0 A. It is located in a uniform magnetic field of 0.420 T inclined at an angle of 30.0° to the wire. What is the magnetic force on the wire? T/I A

MAIN IDEA: You can use the right-hand rule for a moving charge in a magnetic field to determine the direction of the magnetic force on the conductor.

3. Place the labels on **Figure 1** to illustrate the right-hand rule for the magnetic force on a current-carrying wire. K/U

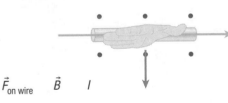

$\vec{F}_{\text{on wire}}$ $\vec{B}$ I

Figure 1

4. The magnetic field of the Earth at a certain spot on the equator is about 45 μT. A wire carries a current from west to east. In which direction is the force on the wire? Explain your answer. T/I A
   (a) up
   (b) down
   (c) east
   (d) no particular direction

STUDY TIP

Modelling a Concept
Using materials to demonstrate or model a concept can help you to understand a concept. Try using your hand and objects representing the wire and current to help you visualize the right-hand rule.

5. A piece of wire 55 cm long has a current of 10.0 A. The wire moves through a uniform magnetic field with a strength of 0.37 T. Calculate the magnitude of the magnetic force on the wire when the angle between the magnetic field and the wire is 45°. K/U T/I

6. A wire 50.0 cm long has a mass of 60.0 g and carries a current of 15.0 A from north to south. It is located in a uniform magnetic field perpendicular to the wire. Determine the minimum magnetic field strength and direction that will balance the weight of the wire. T/I A

7. **Figure 2** is a diagram of a loudspeaker. Label the diagram with the following terms: magnetic material, solenoid, permanent magnet, applied current, speaker cone. K/U

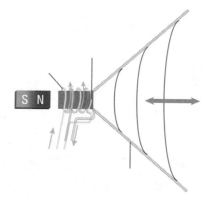

Figure 2

Motion of Charged Particles in Magnetic Fields

Textbook pp. 397–404

> **Vocabulary**
>
> field theory

MAIN IDEA: If a charged particle moves in a uniform magnetic field so that its initial velocity is parallel to the field, it will not experience a magnetic force. If it moves so that its initial velocity is perpendicular to the field, it will move in a circular path in a plane perpendicular to the magnetic field. If a charged particle moves in a uniform magnetic field with a velocity that is neither parallel nor perpendicular to the field, it will move in a spiral path along the field lines. The radius r of the circular path a charged particle takes in a uniform magnetic field can be determined from the equation $r = \dfrac{mv}{qB}$.

1. A charged particle is aimed into a uniform magnetic field perpendicular to the field and follows a circular path. Which of the following is true? Explain your answer. K/U T/I
    (a) A proton follows a path with a smaller radius than an electron.
    (b) The radius of the path decreases as speed increases.
    (c) The radius of the path increases as the field strength decreases.
    (d) all of the above

2. An alpha particle is made up of two protons and two neutrons, and enters a mass spectrometer with a speed of 3.00×10^6 m/s. It follows a circular path that has a radius of 3.40 cm. What is the strength of the magnetic field? T/I A

3. A mass spectrometer known as a calutron is designed to separate fissionable uranium-235 atoms from non-fissionable uranium-238 atoms. The first calutron was built for the Manhattan Project in World War II. The goal of the Manhattan Project was the development of the atomic bomb. ⊤/ᴵ A

   (a) Calculate the ratio of the radius for a U-238 atom compared to that of a U-235 atom.

   (b) The radius of the magnetic field in the calutron was approximately 1.22 m. How far apart were the slits for the two isotopes?

MAIN IDEA: Charged particles entering Earth's magnetic field are deflected and spiral along the field lines toward the magnetic poles. Field theory states that if an object experiences a specific type of force over a continuous range of positions in an area, then a field exists in that area.

4. The light in the aurora borealis is produced by
   (a) collisions between the charged particles from the Sun and atoms in Earth's atmosphere
   (b) the magnetic field of Earth
   (c) radiation from charged particles following a spiral path
   (d) all of the above K/U

5. The Van Allen belts
   (a) have a spherical shape
   (b) consist of charged particles
   (c) are due to the magnetic field of the Sun
   (d) all of the above K/U

8.4 Motion of Charged Particles in Magnetic Fields

Applications of Electric and Magnetic Fields

> **Vocabulary**
>
> radio frequency identification technology (RFID)   magnetic resonance imaging (MRI)
>
> magnetorheological fluid

MAIN IDEA: Radio-frequency identification (RFID) technology is possible through the use of electromagnetic waves, which are a combination of electric and magnetic fields. Magnetorheological (MR) fluid is a fluid of iron particles suspended in a thick liquid that can change state from solid to liquid, and back again when subject to magnetic force.

1. RFID technology
   (a) uses electromagnetic waves to exchange data
   (b) can both transmit and receive information
   (c) uses microchips
   (d) all of the above K/U

2. Why do RFID tags have advantages over bar codes? K/U
   (a) They can be read inside containers and through materials.
   (b) They must be read one at a time.
   (c) They can be embedded in items made of metal.
   (d) all of the above

3. A disadvantage of RFID technology is
   (a) microchips can only be read one at a time
   (b) security of data—unauthorized persons can read the information easily
   (c) microchips must be read by a laser scanner
   (d) all of the above K/U

4. MR fluids
   (a) were invented in the 1990s
   (b) usually contain copper particles in a thick oil
   (c) can turn from liquid to solid using magnetic fields
   (d) all of the above K/U

MAIN IDEA: Current research indicates that exposure to high-voltage electrical fields does not increase the risk of developing certain types of cancers, but research is ongoing. Magnetic resonance imaging (MRI) uses magnetic fields to produce three-dimensional images of internal body systems that provide doctors with clear information about the patient's condition.

5. Exposure to strong electric and magnetic fields
   (a) shows a strong association with adult leukemia
   (b) has been shown to increase the risk of developing brain cancer for young children
   (c) is definitely linked to the development of breast cancer
   (d) shows a weak association with health problems in adults and children K/U

6. Humans are exposed to electromagnetic fields from
   (a) high-voltage power lines
   (b) cellphones
   (c) household appliances
   (d) all of the above K/U

7. MRI
   (a) cannot produce images of soft tissues in the human body
   (b) makes use of magnetic fields
   (c) sends electromagnetic waves through the body to a screen
   (d) all of the above K/U

8. MRI makes use of the fact that
   (a) oxygen atoms in the human body behave like tiny compasses
   (b) atoms in the body always align with an external magnetic field
   (c) there is a small difference in how atoms align with and opposite to a magnetic field among different types of tissue
   (d) all of the above K/U

9. Indicate whether each statement is true or false. If you think the statement is false, rewrite it to make it true. K/U
   (a) MRI makes use of radio waves to spin atoms and align them with an external magnetic field.

   (b) An MRI machine uses radio waves to form an image on a fluorescent screen.

   (c) An advantage of an MRI machine over an X-ray machine is the ability to image soft tissues.

10. Describe how magnetic fields are used in MRIs to generate a three-dimensional image. K/U

Textbook pp. 410–411

Particle Accelerators

MAIN IDEA: Particle accelerators use electric and magnetic fields to accelerate sub-atomic particles to high speeds. The particles are then smashed into atoms or each other to form other particles.

> **LEARNING TIP**
>
> **Particle Accelerators**
> Distinguish between a linear or circular accelerator by using labelled diagrams and a comparison chart.

1. A linear particle accelerator
   (a) moves charged particles in a straight path
   (b) confines charged particles in a narrow beam using electromagnets
   (c) accelerates charged particles in a vacuum
   (d) all of the above K/U

2. The longest linear accelerator currently in use has a length of
   (a) several kilometres
   (b) several metres
   (c) several centimetres
   (d) several millimetres K/U

3. Circular accelerators
   (a) use permanent magnets made of iron to accelerate particles
   (b) include the TRIUMF cyclotron at the University of British Columbia
   (c) send particles exactly once around the track before smashing them into a target
   (d) all of the above K/U

4. Particle accelerators
   (a) were used in the picture tubes of older televisions
   (b) are only found in research establishments, such as universities, due to their high cost
   (c) are always very large and require very large buildings
   (d) consume many megawatts of power K/U

5. The Large Hadron Collider is located in
   (a) the United States
   (b) Canada
   (c) Japan
   (d) Switzerland K/U

6. Is the following statement true or false? If you think the statement is false, rewrite it to make it true: A hospital can use a particle accelerator for radiotherapy. K/U

Magnetic Fields

Use the graphic organizer below to summarize what you have learned about magnetic fields. Add lines to connect concepts. You can add your own notes, diagrams, and equations to this graphic organizer, creating a study tool to help you review Chapter 8.

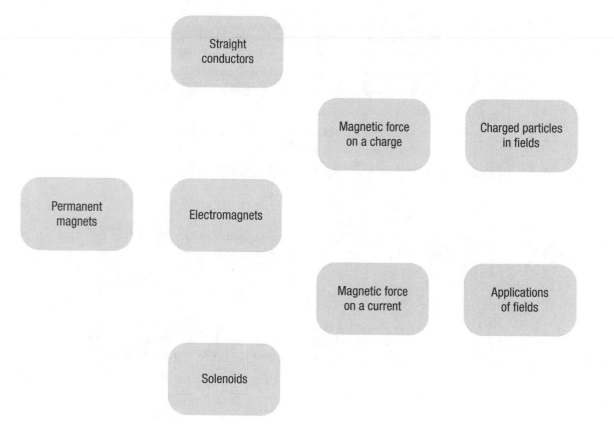

K/U   Knowledge/Understanding
T/I   Thinking/Investigation
C   Communication
A   Application

1. A magnetic field runs from west to east. An electron is placed in the field. The magnetic force on the electron
   (a) equals zero
   (b) points to the north
   (c) points to the south
   (d) points perpendicular to the magnetic field (8.2) K/U

2. The force on a current-carrying conductor in a magnetic field
   (a) was discovered by Volta
   (b) is applied in the operation of electric motors
   (c) is equal to zero if the conductor is perpendicular to the field
   (d) all of the above (8.3) K/U

3. Indicate whether each statement is true or false. If you think the statement is false, rewrite it to make it true. K/U
   (a) Magnetic field lines always form closed loops. (8.1)

   (b) An electron that is shot into a magnetic field parallel to the field lines will follow a spiral path around the lines. (8.4)

4. The magnetic field of Earth is approximately 45.0 μT. A cosmic ray proton moving at 5 % of the speed of light crosses the field at an angle of 60.0°. What is the magnetic force acting on the proton? (8.2) T/I A

5. A wire in a motor is 4.20 cm long and carries a current of 1.85 A. It is located in a uniform magnetic field inclined at an angle of 45.0° to the wire. If the wire experiences a force of 3.42 N, what is the strength of the magnetic field? (8.3) T/I A

6. A uranium-235 ion has a charge of $2e$. It enters a mass spectrometer perpendicular to a magnetic field of 3.86 T at a speed of 2.14×10^5 m/s. What is the radius of its path in the spectrometer? (8.4) T/I A

7. Two protons moving at v and $2v$ enter a uniform magnetic field perpendicular to the field. How do the radii of their paths compare? (8.4) T/I A

8. Discuss one application of magnetic fields. (8.5) K/U C

1. An example of a satellite with a geosynchronous orbit is
   (a) a GPS satellite
   (b) the Moon
   (c) a commercial satellite used for home satellite television signals
   (d) all of the above (6.2) K/U

2. The electric potential due to a point charge
   (a) is inversely proportional to the amount of charge producing the field
   (b) is directly proportional to the distance from the charge producing the field
   (c) approaches zero at great distances from the charge producing the field
   (d) all of the above (7.5) K/U

3. A mass spectrometer can be used to
   (a) identify unknown compounds
   (b) determine the structure of a compound
   (c) determine the isotopic makeup of molecular elements
   (d) all of the above (8.4) K/U

4. Indicate whether each statement is true or false. If you think the statement is false, rewrite it to make it true. K/U
   (a) The gravitational field of Earth increases as the inverse square of the distance from Earth. (6.1)

   (b) Every subatomic particle detected so far has a charge whose magnitude is a whole-number multiple of the charge on a proton. (7.6)

   (c) Magnetorheological fluids used in the construction of a building can help protect the building against earthquake damage. (8.5)

5. An astronomical unit (AU) is defined as the mean distance from Earth to the Sun, or 1.50×10^{11} m. The dwarf planet Eris was discovered in 2005 orbiting 96.6 AU from the Sun, about three times as far out as Pluto. What is the mean speed of orbit for Eris? (6.2) T/I A

6. Two point charges experience an electric force F between them when separated by a distance d. The magnitude of each charge is doubled. How must the distance between the charges be adjusted such that the magnitude of the force remains unchanged? (7.2) T/I A

7. An oxygen ion has a charge of $3e$. It contains eight protons and eight neutrons. It is accelerated in a linear accelerator to a speed of 4.00×10^3 m/s. It is then shot into a magnetic field of 6.34 T at an angle of 20.0° to the field. What is the magnetic force on the ion? (8.2) T/I A

The Wave Nature of Light

UNIT 4

BIG IDEAS

- Light has properties that are similar to the properties of mechanical waves.

- The behaviour of light as a wave can be described mathematically.

- Many technologies that use the principles of the wave nature of light can have societal and environmental implications.

Chapter 9: Waves and Light

A wave is a moving disturbance that transports energy from one place to another, but does not transport matter. The speed of a periodic wave equals its wavelength times its frequency. This is the universal wave equation.

When light reflects off a surface, the angle of incidence of the light onto the surface equals the angle of reflection of light as it passes through a medium.

Snell's law relates the angle of incidence and the angle of refraction. The index of refraction of a medium is the ratio of the speed of light in a vacuum to the speed of light in the medium. Wavelength decreases as the index of refraction increases. Frequency remains constant. Different frequencies may have different indices of refraction in a given medium. This leads to light dispersion or separation into colours.

Total internal reflection occurs when light is transiting from one medium to a less optically dense medium at an angle of incidence greater than the critical angle, which is the angle of incidence that results in a 90° angle of refraction.

Diffraction is the bending and spreading of a wave whose wavelength is less than or comparable to the size of the slit or obstacle that the wave passes through.

Interference occurs when two or more waves meet. If a crest meets a crest, constructive interference occurs. If a crest meets a trough, destructive interference occurs. Waves with shorter wavelengths diffract less than waves with longer wavelengths. A pair of identical point sources in phase produces a symmetrical pattern of constructive interference areas and nodal lines.

Newton proposed the particle theory of light. Huygens and others supported the wave theory of light. Both explain some, but not all, properties of light. Young's experiment demonstrated that light diffracts and interferes to produce diffraction patterns similar to those of water waves in a ripple tank. It supported the wave theory of light.

Chapter 10: Applications of the Wave Nature of Light

Light waves invert when reflected from the boundary of a medium that has a higher index of refraction than the original medium. No phase change occurs when light waves move toward a medium with a lower index of refraction. Light waves that reflect from the two surfaces of a thin film produce interference fringes that depend on the difference in path length and the number of phase changes that occur.

Monochromatic light passing through a single slit produces a diffraction pattern. The resolution of an optical instrument refers to its ability to separate closely spaced objects into distinct images. A diffraction grating consists of a large number of closely spaced parallel slits. It produces an interference pattern similar to that from a double-slit experiment.

Maxwell predicted the existence of electromagnetic waves that consist of alternating electric and magnetic fields. The existence was confirmed by Hertz in his experiments with radio waves. The electric and magnetic fields are perpendicular to each other and the direction of propagations of the waves. Light is an example of an electromagnetic wave phenomenon.

Polarized light uses filters to selectively block the transmission of light waves. Linearly polarized light is entirely polarized in one direction that is perpendicular to the direction of propagation.

Properties of Waves and Light

Vocabulary		
periodic wave	phase	angle of incidence
wave front	ray approximation	angle of reflection
crest	reflection	specular reflection
trough	normal	diffuse reflection
wavelength (λ)		

Textbook pp. 440–443

MAIN IDEA: A wave is a moving disturbance that transports energy from one place to another but does not transport matter. The speed of a wave is related to its wavelength and frequency by the universal wave equation, $v = f\lambda$.

1. One end of a rope is attached to a building. The other end is waved up and down at a frequency of 4.0 Hz (**Figure 1**). Estimate the wave properties listed. Axis units are in metres. K/U A

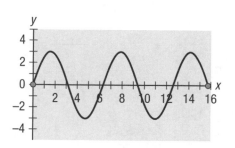

Figure 1

amplitude: _____
wavelength: _____
period: _____
speed: _____

2. A microwave oven operates at a frequency of 2.45 GHz. The waves travel at 3.00×10^8 m/s. What is the wavelength? T/I A

3. The highest recorded ocean waves were observed by a U.S. Navy ship in the north Pacific Ocean in 1933. The amplitude was 34 m, the period was 14.8 s, and the wavelength was 342 m. How fast were the waves travelling? T/I A

MAIN IDEA: To determine the change in direction of a light ray after it reflects off of a surface, measure the angle between the incident ray and the normal to the reflecting surface, and the angle between the reflected ray and the normal to the reflecting surface. The law of reflection states that the angle of incidence θ_i is equal to the angle of reflection θ_r, $\theta_i = \theta_r$.

4. Correctly place the following labels on **Figure 2** below. K/U

incident ray   reflecting surface

normal θ_i

reflected ray θ_r

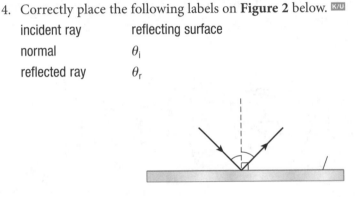

Figure 2

5. Is the following statement true or false? If you think the statement is false, rewrite it to make it true: The law of reflection does not apply to diffuse reflections. K/U

6. The depth of the water at a point on a lake can be determined by sending a high-frequency sound wave vertically to the bottom of the lake, and timing how long it takes for the sound waves to return. This is called SONAR, for sound navigation and ranging. A typical SONAR set operates at 192 kHz, and has a wavelength of 0.772 cm. If a signal returns 0.264 s after it is sent, how deep is the water? T/I A

Refraction and Total Internal Reflection

Textbook pp. 444–458

Vocabulary

refraction	angle of refraction	critical angle
optical density	dispersion	total internal reflection
principle of reversibility	angle of deviation	fibre optics
index of refraction		

MAIN IDEA: Snell's law describes the relationship between the incident and refracted angles of a light ray and the indices of refraction of two media: $n_1 \sin \theta_1 = n_2 \sin \theta_2$. The index of refraction, n, of a medium is the ratio of the speed of light in a vacuum, c, to the speed of light in the medium, v: $n = \dfrac{c}{v}$.

1. **Figure 1** shows a ray of light crossing the boundary between two media, 1 and 2. Which medium has the higher index of refraction? Explain your answer. K/U

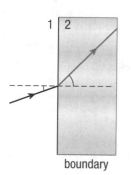

boundary

Figure 1

> ### STUDY **TIP**
>
> **Graphic Organizers**
> Keep important information close at hand. Use file cards to organize information in tables, charts, or diagrams.

2. A ray of light crosses from air into diamond at an angle of incidence of 30.0°. Diamond has an index of refraction of 2.42. Determine the angle of refraction. T/I A

3. The cornea of the human eye has an index of refraction of about 1.38. How fast is light travelling as it transits the cornea? T/I A

4. The index of refraction for benzene is approximately 1.50. In air, a red light ray has a wavelength of 600 nm and a frequency of 5.00×10^{14} Hz. What is the wavelength and frequency of red light in benzene? Explain your answer. K/U A
   (a) 600 nm and 5.00×10^{14} Hz
   (b) 400 nm and 5.00×10^{14} Hz
   (c) 600 nm and 3.33×10^{14} Hz
   (d) 400 nm and 3.33×10^{14} Hz

MAIN IDEA: The index of refraction, n, of a medium is equal to the ratio of the wavelength of light in a vacuum, λ_1, to the wavelength of light in the medium, λ_2, $n = \dfrac{\lambda_1}{\lambda_2}$. For two different media, $\dfrac{n_1}{n_2} = \dfrac{\lambda_2}{\lambda_1}$. The frequency of light remains the same in all media.

5. A ray of light with a wavelength of 540 nm goes from air into zircon. What is the wavelength in zircon? The index of refraction for zircon is 1.92. T/I A

MAIN IDEA: Dispersion is the separation of a wave into its component parts according to a given characteristic, such as wavelength. When light passes from one medium to another, partial reflection and partial refraction can occur, and the wavelength changes based upon the index of refraction for the second medium. Total internal reflection occurs when light is completely reflected at a boundary between two media. The incident light must originate in the more optically dense medium, and the angle of incidence must be greater than the critical angle. The critical angle can be calculated using $\theta_c = \sin^{-1}\left(\dfrac{n_2}{n_1}\right)$.

6. A gemstone such as a diamond often sparkles with different colours. What property causes the colours? K/U
   (a) total internal reflection
   (b) the low index of refraction of diamond
   (c) dispersion
   (d) the law of reflection

7. Gemma is sitting on the bottom of a swimming pool. As she looks upward and down the pool, she sees the bottom of the pool reflected in the surface of the water. This is due to
   (a) light reaching the boundary with a less refractive medium
   (b) total internal reflection
   (c) her viewing angle is greater than the critical angle
   (d) all of the above K/U

8. A Pyrex glass rod is placed in water. Determine the critical angle for a ray of light moving from the Pyrex into the water. T/I A

Diffraction and Interference of Water Waves

Textbook pp. 459–469

Vocabulary		
diffraction	destructive interference	nodal line
interference	coherent	path length
constructive interference	node	path length difference

MAIN IDEA: Diffraction is the bending and spreading of a wave whose wavelength is less than or comparable to the size of the slit or obstacle that the wave passes, or where $\frac{\lambda}{w} \leq 1$. Interference occurs when two waves in the same medium meet. Constructive interference occurs when the crest of one wave meets the crest of another wave. Destructive interference occurs when the crest of one wave meets the trough of another wave. Waves with shorter wavelengths diffract less than waves with longer wavelengths.

> **STUDY TIP**
>
> **Meanings of Terms**
> Although the two terms often occur in the same sentence, do not confuse diffraction and interference. It is possible to have diffraction without interference, and interference without diffraction.

1. Two loudspeakers are set up 10.0 m apart for a school dance, and are fed from the same sound source that produces a steady test sound of frequency 800 Hz. A student walks between the two speakers to check the acoustics. As she changes her position, the sound seems loud in some places, but soft in others. The loud sounds are due to _____ and the soft sounds are due to _____. Explain your answer. K/U T/I

   (a) constructive interference, destructive interference
   (b) destructive interference, constructive interference
   (c) diffraction, refraction
   (d) diffraction, dispersion

2. A breakwall protecting a harbour has a gap 5 m wide to allow small watercraft to pass through. On Monday, waves with a wavelength of 4 m pass through the gap. On Tuesday, waves of wavelength 1 m pass through the gap. Will an observer see more wave diffraction on Monday or Tuesday? Explain your answer. T/I A

MAIN IDEA: A pair of identical point sources that are in phase produce a symmetrical pattern of constructive interference areas and nodal lines. The number of nodal lines in a given region will increase when the frequency of vibration of the sources increases or when the wavelength decreases. When the separation of the sources increases, the number of nodal lines also increases. The relationship that can be used to solve for an unknown variable in a two-point-source interference pattern is $|P_nS_1 - P_nS_2| = \left(n - \frac{1}{2}\right)\lambda$.

3. The distance from the right bisector to a point P on the second nodal line in a two-point interference pattern is 5.0 cm. The distance from the midpoint between the two sources, which are 0.6 cm apart, to point P is 15 cm. Calculate the angle θ_2 for the second nodal line. T/I A

4. Two identical sources in phase, each with amplitude A, produce the interference pattern shown in **Figure 1**. Below is a list of labels. Add the labels in their correct places. [K/U]

lines of destructive interference (nodal lines)   amplitude here is $2A$ crests

areas of constructive interference   amplitude here is $-2A$ troughs

node

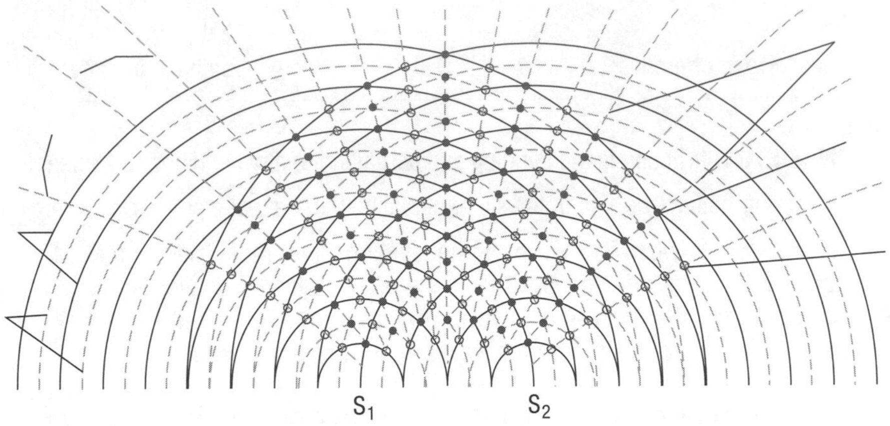

S_1 S_2

Figure 1

5. Two sources are 10.0 cm apart. An interference pattern is observed at a distance of 25.0 cm along the right bisector of the line segment joining the sources. The third nodal line is 33.6 cm from the right bisector at this distance. What is the wavelength of the waves? [T/I] [A]

6. Waves of wavelength 8.12 cm are produced by two sources vibrating in phase with the same amplitude. What is the path length difference for a point on the fourth nodal line from the centre of the interference pattern? [T/I] [A]

Light: Wave or Particle?

Vocabulary	
Huygens' principle	rectilinear propagation

MAIN IDEA: Newton proposed the particle theory of light to explain reflection, refraction, and the rectilinear propagation of light. However, Newton's theory could not adequately explain diffraction.

1. A major supporter of the wave theory of light was
   (a) Grimaldi
   (b) Hooke
   (c) Huygens
   (d) all of the above [K/U]

2. Newton concluded that the particles that make up light
   (a) move at very high speeds
   (b) each have a large mass
   (c) produce a noticeable pressure
   (d) all of the above [K/U]

3. Did Young's double-slit experiment provide support for the particle theory of light or the wave theory of light? Explain your answer. [K/U] [A]

> **STUDY TIP**
>
> **Understanding New Vocabulary**
> Sometime long words can be intimidating. However, if you view the word in familiar parts, you can most often determine the meaning of the word. For example,
> rectilinear = recti + linear
> recti = straight and linear = line
> So, rectilinear means straight lines.

4. Newton explained refraction as a result of particles speeding up when moving from air to glass, and, hence, bending towards the normal. In fact, light slows down when moving from air to glass. Why did Newton not correct his error? [K/U] [A]

MAIN IDEA: Huygens' principle states that every point on a wave front acts as a point source for secondary wavelets, which then spread out in front of the initial wave at the same speed. The new wave front appears as a line tangent to all the wavelets. The wave theory proposed by Huygens and embodied in Huygens' principle explains reflection, refraction, and diffraction.

5. According to Huygens' wave theory of light, what statement is true about light crossing from air into water? [K/U]
   (a) The speed decreases.
   (b) The wavelength increases.
   (c) The frequency increases.
   (d) all of the above

6. Is the following statement true or false? If you think the statement is false, rewrite it to make it true: Huygens' principle applies only to straight wave fronts. [K/U]

7. Suleiman is standing near the corner of a building. He can hear Indira and Polina talking around the corner, but he cannot see them. Explain why this happens. Illustrate your answer with a diagram. T/I C A

8. Write the labels listed below on **Figure 1**. T/I C A
   direction of propagation
   virtual sources
   wave front

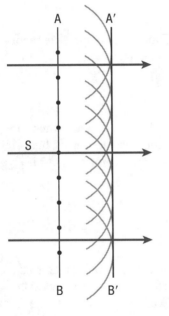

Figure 1

Interference of Light Waves: Young's Double-Slit Experiment

Textbook pp. 477–484

Vocabulary

incoherent

monochromatic

interference fringe

maxima

minima

MAIN IDEA: Young's experiment produced a series of light and dark fringes on a screen placed in the path of the light, with a pattern that resembled the results of interference of water waves in a ripple tank.

1. Early experiments to demonstrate diffraction of light did not succeed. Why not? K/U
   (a) The nodal lines were too far apart to observe.
   (b) The wavelength of light was too large.
   (c) The sources were not in phase.
   (d) all of the above

2. An example of a monochromatic light source is a(n)
   (a) incandescent light bulb
   (b) fluorescent light
   (c) neon light
   (d) laser K/U

3. Is the following statement true or false? If you think the statement is false, rewrite it to make it true: A monochromatic light source must be coherent. K/U

STUDY TIP

Equations for Double-Slit Interference

When adding the equations for double-slit interference to your equation sheet, be careful to indicate where each equation applies. It is easy to confuse the equation that applies to dark fringes with the equation that applies to bright fringes.

MAIN IDEA: The locations of bright fringes are given by $d \sin \theta = m\lambda$, $m = 0, 1, 2, 3, \ldots$. The locations of dark fringes are given by $d \sin \theta = \left(n - \dfrac{1}{2} \right)\lambda$, $n = 0, 1, 2, 3, \ldots$. For a viewing screen at a distance L, the mth-order bright fringe is at location $x_m = \dfrac{mL\lambda}{d}$. The nth-order dark fringe is at location $x_n = \left(n - \dfrac{1}{2} \right)\dfrac{L\lambda}{d}$. Young's diffraction experiment provided evidence for the wave nature of light.

4. After Young succeeded in demonstrating diffraction and interference in light, the wave theory could explain all properties of light except one. Which was it? K/U
   (a) refraction
   (b) rectilinear propagation
   (c) propagation through a vacuum
   (d) dispersion

5. Is the following statement true or false? If you think the statement is false, rewrite it to make it true: If the slits producing an interference pattern can be moved closer together, the bright fringes will move farther apart. K/U

6. A double-slit experiment is carried out with a slit spacing of 0.39 mm. The screen is at a distance of 1.4 m. The bright fringes at the centre of the screen are separated by 1.3 mm. Calculate the wavelength of the light. T/I

7. Two slits are separated by a distance of 3.20×10^{-6} m and illuminated with a monochromatic light. The second-order bright fringe is observed at an angle of 19.0°. What is the wavelength of the light? T/I A

8. A double-slit experiment using red light of wavelength 640 nm results in a second-order bright fringe at $x_{2r} = 0.442$ mm. If the light source is changed to ultraviolet with half the wavelength, where will the second-order bright fringe be located? T/I A

Explore an Issue in Light-Based Technology

Should Governments Restrict Network Access?

Textbook pp. 485–486

MAIN IDEA: Fibre optic technology uses light to transmit large volumes of data quickly across great distances. Large amounts of diverse data are available to the general public via a global network known as the Internet.

1. Fibre optic technology operates primarily on which principle? K/U
   (a) total internal reflection
   (b) dispersion
   (c) propagation through a vacuum
   (d) all of the above

2. Arguments in favour of restricting access to information include
   (a) security issues
   (b) privacy issues
   (c) copyright issues
   (d) all of the above K/U A

3. Indicate whether the following statement is true or false. If you think the statement is false, rewrite it to make it true. Some governments are working towards making broadband access available to all citizens. K/U

4. Annotate and extend the graphic organizer shown below to illustrate the controversy surrounding unrestricted access to information. K/U

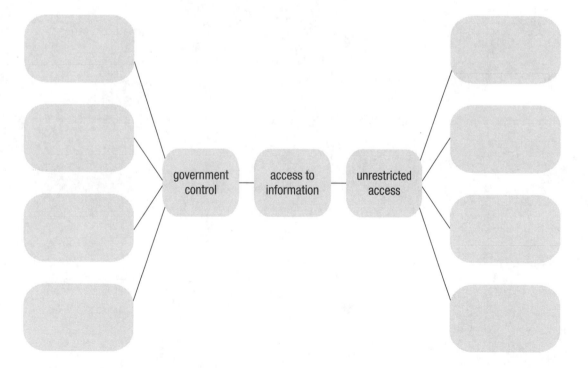

Waves and Light

Use the graphic organizer below to summarize what you have learned about waves and light. Connect the concepts. You can add your own notes, diagrams, and equations to this graphic organizer, creating a study tool to help you review Chapter 9.

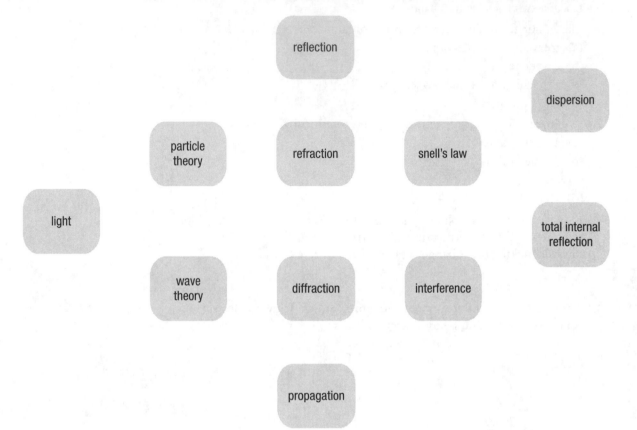

1. Which of the below is an example of electromagnetic radiation? (9.1) K/U
   (a) visible light from the Sun
   (b) sound from a loudspeaker
   (c) X-rays
   (d) both (a) and (c)

2. Which devices use light rays in their operation? (9.1) K/U A
   (a) fibre optic lines for data transfer
   (b) DVD players
   (c) photocells on garage door openers
   (d) all of the above

3. Indicate whether each statement is true or false. If you think the statement is false, rewrite it to make it true. K/U
   (a) The properties of refraction are correctly explained using the wave theory of light, but not using the particle theory. (9.4)

   (b) Fibre optic technology cannot be applied to telephone communications, which must use copper wires to carry an electrical signal. (9.6)

4. A scuba diver aims an underwater light at the water's surface with an angle of incidence of 25.0°. The index of refraction of the water is 1.33. Determine the angle of refraction. (9.2) T/I A

5. Two magnetrons are producing microwaves of wavelength 12.0 cm in phase. An interference pattern is analyzed at a distance of 3.25 m along the right bisector of the line segment joining the sources. The fifth nodal line is 82.6 cm from the right bisector at this distance. What is the distance between the sources? (9.3) T/I A

K/U	Knowledge/Understanding
T/I	Thinking/Investigation
C	Communication
A	Application

6. Light waves of length 440 nm are sent through two slits. What is the path difference for a point on the third nodal line from the centre of the interference pattern? (9.3) [T/I] [A]

7. Two slits are separated by a distance of 5.60×10^{-6} m and illuminated with a monochromatic light of wavelength 480 nm. What is the angle for the third-order bright fringe? (9.5) [T/I] [A]

8. Two slits are separated by a distance of 4.40×10^{-6} m and illuminated with two monochromatic light sources with wavelengths of 600 nm (red) and 400 nm (violet). The m_rth bright fringe of the red light coincides with the m_vth bright fringe of the violet light. What are the lowest possible values for m_r and m_v? (9.5) [T/I] [A]

Interference in Thin Films

Vocabulary

thin film   air wedge

Textbook pp. 502–511

MAIN IDEA: Light waves become inverted when they reflect from the boundary of a medium that has a higher index of refraction than the original medium. No phase change occurs when light waves reflect from the boundary of a medium that has a lower index of refraction than the original medium. Light waves that reflect from the two surfaces of a thin film produce interference fringes that depend on the different path lengths travelled by the two waves, the wavelength of the light, any phase changes that occur from reflection, and the indices of refraction for the materials involved.

1. Which of the following is an example of interference in a thin film? **K/U**

   (a) colours formed by a layer of oil on water

   (b) Young's double-slit experiment

   (c) the spectrum formed by a triangular prism

   (d) all of the above

2. A light wave meets the boundary between glass and air at an angle of incidence of 10.0°. Part of the wave is transmitted to the air and part is reflected back into the glass. The transmitted wave will undergo _____ while the reflected wave will undergo _____. Explain your answer. **K/U**

   (a) a phase change, a phase change

   (b) a phase change, no phase change

   (c) no phase change, a phase change

   (d) no phase change, no phase change

STUDY TIP

Graphic Organizer
Thin film interference can be confusing since there could be as many as three indices of refraction involved. Use a graphic organizer to list the indices, and determine whether a phase change occurs. Here is a sample:

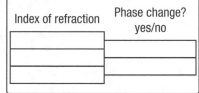

3. Is the following statement true or false? If you think the statement is false, rewrite it to make it true: As the optical density of a medium increases, the speed of light in the medium increases. **K/U**

4. Water has an index of refraction of 1.33. Green light has a wavelength of about 532 nm in air. What is the wavelength of green light in water? **T/I** **A**

MAIN IDEA: If only one wave undergoes a phase change, $2t = \dfrac{\left(m + \frac{1}{2}\right)\lambda}{n_{film}}$, $m = 0, 1, 2, 3, \ldots$ for constructive interference and $2t = \dfrac{n\lambda}{n_{film}}$, $n = 1, 2, 3, \ldots$ for destructive interference. If both waves undergo a phase change, $2t = \dfrac{n\lambda}{n_{film}}$, $n = 1, 2, 3, \ldots$ for constructive interference and $2t = \dfrac{\left(m + \frac{1}{2}\right)\lambda}{n_{film}}$, $m = 0, 1, 2, 3, \ldots$ for destructive interference. Newton's rings and fringes in air wedges result from light reflecting, transmitting, and interfering with surfaces that have different separations at different locations.

5. A thin layer of polycarbonate with an index of refraction of 1.59 is placed on a glass screen to protect it from abrasion. The index of refraction of glass is 1.50. When illuminated with white light, the polycarbonate reflects yellow light with a wavelength of 580 nm. What is the lowest possible value for the thickness of the polycarbonate layer? T/I A

6. Two glass plates are in contact at one edge but separated on the other edge with a piece of gold foil 1.80×10^{-6} m thick. The plates are illuminated with a monochromatic light source, and an observer counts eight bright and eight dark fringes along the top plate. Determine the wavelength of the light. T/I A

Single-Slit Diffraction

Textbook pp. 512–519

Vocabulary

Fraunhofer diffraction   central maximum   secondary maxima   resolution

MAIN IDEA: Monochromatic light passing through a single slit produces a diffraction pattern that consists of a bright central region surrounded by alternating light and dark bands resulting from constructive and destructive interference. Fraunhofer diffraction is a special case of diffraction that shows distinctive differences between the central fringe and darker flanking fringes.

1. Which condition is necessary for Fraunhofer diffraction? **K/U**
   (a) The width of the slit is narrow enough to cause substantial diffraction, but not narrow enough to act as a single source of waves.
   (b) The light source is monochromatic.
   (c) The light source is far from the slit.
   (d) all of the above

2. Is the following statement true or false? If you think the statement is false, rewrite it to make it true: The interference pattern produced by a single slit is a result of Huygens' principle. **K/U**

> **LEARNING TIP**
>
> **Mathematical Modelling**
> When reviewing the derivation for single-slit interference, use 12 virtual sources for Huygens' principle. This allows an easy argument up to the fourth off-centre maximum.

MAIN IDEA: In single-slit diffraction, the dark bands occur at angles θ_n such that $\sin \theta_n = \dfrac{n\lambda}{w}$ $(n = 1, 2,...)$; the bright bands occur at angles θ_m such that $\sin \theta_m = \dfrac{\left(m + \dfrac{1}{2}\right)\lambda}{w}$ $(m = 1, 2,...)$. The distance between successive minima, and successive maxima, is given by $\Delta y = \dfrac{\lambda L}{w}$. The width of the central maximum is $2\Delta y$.

3. The resolution of an optical device is limited by
   (a) the wavelength of the light that passes through it
   (b) the size of the smallest aperture in the device
   (c) overlapping diffraction patterns from sources that are too close together
   (d) all of the above **K/U**

4. Light of wavelength 462 nm illuminates a single slit with a width of 12.4 μm. A diffraction pattern appears 0.750 m behind the slit. What is the location of the first bright band after the central maximum? **K/U** **T/I** **A**

Dimensional Analysis
When writing mathematical solutions
to a problem, you can save time if
you determine which units can be
cancelled without having to convert
the unit to a common unit.

5. A rectangular room measures 3.00 m by 4.00 m. A 25.0 cm wide source of
microwaves with a wavelength of 15.0 cm is placed in the centre of the longer
side and produces an interference pattern on the opposite wall. At what
location(s) along this wall would the minima of the microwave radiation
appear? T/I A

6. A monochromatic light source illuminates a single slit with a width of 8.34 μm.
The third bright band appears 13.0° from the central maximum. What is the
wavelength of the light? T/I A

7. A single slit is illuminated by a blue light source with a wavelength of 450 nm
and a red light source with a wavelength of 600.0 nm. What are the smallest
values for n_{blue} and n_{red} such that a dark band from the blue light is in the same
position as a dark band from the red light? T/I A

The Diffraction Grating

Vocabulary

diffraction grating   zero-order maximum   first-order maximum   order number

Textbook pp. 520–525

MAIN IDEA: A diffraction grating consists of a large number of closely spaced parallel slits. Diffraction gratings produce interference patterns that are similar to those from a double slit, but the maxima are far narrower and more intense.

1. A diffraction grating can separate light into colours. How does this happen? **K/U**
   (a) The grating uses refraction to disperse the colours, similar to a prism.
   (b) Each of the slits is individually adjusted to respond to a particular wavelength of light.
   (c) The separation results from different colours diffracting through different angles.
   (d) all of the above

2. Modern manufacturing of diffraction gratings
   (a) is often done by hand by highly skilled craftsmen
   (b) can be done using lasers and photographic film
   (c) typically results in 10 to 20 lines per centimetre
   (d) results in a grating that will only work with a specific wavelength of light **K/U**

3. Indicate whether each statement is true or false. If you think the statement is false, rewrite it to make it true. **K/U**
   (a) A DVD is an example of a transmission diffraction grating.

   (b) As the slit separation in a grating increases, the maxima in the interference pattern become broader.

> ### STUDY TIP
>
> **Format of Variables**
> Sometimes you may be confused between a variable and an abbreviated measurement unit. Remember: variables are italicized and measurement units are not.

MAIN IDEA: The angle, θ_m, for the mth-order maximum of a diffraction grating with slit spacing w and light wavelength λ is given by $m\lambda = w \sin \theta_m$.

4. CDs and DVDs have some important similarities and some important differences. Use a graphic organizer to compare the similarities and differences. **K/U** **C**

5. A diffraction grating has 6400 lines/cm. It is illuminated with light from a monochromatic light source. The third order maximum is located at an angle of 70.0°. What is the wavelength of the light? T/I A

6. Light is emitted by a sodium vapour lamp with a wavelength of 589 nm. It falls on a diffraction grating with 7600 lines/cm. Determine the angle at which the second maximum occurs. T/I A

7. A diffraction grating has 4200 lines/cm. Maxima up to order 5 are observed. What is the maximum wavelength possible for the light illuminating the grating? T/I A

Electromagnetic Radiation

Vocabulary

electromagnetic radiation

electromagnetic spectrum

Textbook pp. 526–531

MAIN IDEA: Maxwell's theory of electromagnetism predicts that oscillating electric and magnetic fields propagate through space at the speed of light. Hertz experimentally confirmed the existence of electromagnetic waves. Electromagnetic waves are produced by accelerating electric charges and consist of magnetic and electric fields that are perpendicular to each other and to the direction of propagation. Electromagnetic waves oscillate in phase.

1. Which of these are a form of electromagnetic radiation? K/U
   (i)   microwaves in a microwave oven
   (ii) the output of a laser in a DVD player
   (iii) the sound from a pair of loudspeakers
   (iv) infrared emitted from a television remote control
   (a) i, ii   (b) i, ii, iii   (c) i, ii, iv   (d) all of these

2. An electric charge at rest in space produces
   (a) an electric field
   (b) a magnetic field
   (c) both an electric field and a magnetic field, perpendicular to each other
   (d) neither an electric field nor a magnetic field K/U

3. **Figure 1** represents an electromagnetic wave moving through space. Label Figure 1 with the following terms.

   λ (wavelength)

   c (speed and direction of propagation)

   $\vec{\varepsilon}$ (electric field)

   $\vec{B}$ (magnetic field)

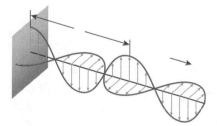

Figure 1

> **STUDY TIP**
>
> **Use the Internet**
> If you have trouble visualizing the propagation of electromagnetic waves in three dimensions, search the Internet for videos. Search using the keywords *electromagnetic waves animation*. Run one or more of the simulations.

4. Is the following statement true or false? If you think the statement is false, rewrite it to make it true: Electromagnetic waves will travel through a vacuum. K/U

MAIN IDEA: The electromagnetic spectrum is the range of all possible electromagnetic radiation of various wavelengths and frequencies. The main categories of waves in the electromagnetic spectrum are radio waves, microwaves, visible light, ultraviolet light, infrared light, X-rays, and gamma rays.

5. Gamma rays have the _____ wavelength and the _____ frequency of the commonly named waves in the electromagnetic spectrum. **K/U**
   (a) longest, highest
   (b) shortest, highest
   (c) longest, lowest
   (d) shortest, lowest

6. Select the correct phrase to complete the statement. What is the highest possible frequency for electromagnetic waves? Explain your answer. **K/U**
   (a) 10^4 Hz
   (b) 10^{14} Hz
   (c) 10^{23} Hz
   (d) There is no limit on the frequency.

7. Very Low Frequency (VLF) radio waves are used to communicate with submarines because they can transmit through water. If a VLF wave has a frequency of 10.0 kHz, what is the wavelength? **T/I** **A**

8. An FM radio station uses a frequency of 88.1 MHz. A gamma ray emitted by a radioactive nucleus has a frequency of 1.00×10^{22} Hz. How does the energy of the gamma ray compare to the energy of the radio wave? **T/I** **C** **A**

Polarization of Light

Vocabulary

polarized light

unpolarized light

polarizer

linearly polarized (plane polarized)

transmission axis

analyzer

Malus's Law

Brewster's angle

scattering

optical activity

liquid crystal display (LCD)

Textbook pp. 532–537

MAIN IDEA: Polarized light uses filters to selectively block the transmission of light waves. You can use a sheet of Polaroid material to produce polarized light, to detect if light is polarized, and to determine the direction of polarization. Linearly polarized, or plane polarized, light is entirely polarized in one direction that is perpendicular to the direction of propagation. Reflection and scattering are two ways that polarized light can be produced from unpolarized light.

1. Which source produces electromagnetic waves that can be polarized? K/U
   (a) the Sun
   (b) a microwave oven
   (c) an X-ray machine
   (d) all of the above

2. Write the following labels in their correct positions on **Figure 1** below. K/U

   polarized light

   unpolarized light

   source

   polarizer

> **STUDY TIP**
>
> **New Terms**
> Use diagrams to help you understand new terms.

Figure 1

3. Is the following statement true or false? If you think the statement is false, rewrite it to make it true: The primary advantage of polarized sunglasses over unpolarized sunglasses is that they reduce glare reflected from surfaces such as the surface of a lake. K/U

MAIN IDEA: Malus's law states how the transmitted intensity of light through a polarizer is related to the incident intensity of light: $I_{out} = I_{in} \cos^2\theta$. Polarization filters have many uses, including stress analysis in materials, sunglasses, and the design and production of LCD displays. Simple sugars, such as fructose and sucrose, are optically active molecules that rotate in the direction of the polarization of light. By applying different voltages to different areas of the liquid crystal, an LCD device can form various patterns of light and dark regions corresponding to letters or numbers.

4. The blue colour of the sky is due to _____ of light from the Sun.
   Observing the sky through a polarizer makes it appear _____ . K/U
   (a) polarization, darker blue   (c) scattering, darker blue
   (b) polarization, lighter blue   (d) scattering, lighter blue

5. Is the following statement true or false? If you think the statement is false, rewrite it to make it true: A polarizer blocks half of the unpolarized light that passes through it. K/U

6. An optically active transparent material
   (a) usually contains molecules with a helical structure
   (b) is always a simple sugar, such as fructose or sucrose
   (c) plane polarizes light passing through it
   (d) all of the above K/U

7. A ray of light is plane polarized. A polarizer is placed with its polarizing axis at an angle of 30.0° to the polarization of the incident ray. What fraction of the original intensity of the ray is transmitted through the polarizer? T/I A

8. Silicon has an index of refraction of 3.96. A ray of light moving through air is directed onto a flat piece of silicon. The reflected ray is completely polarized. What is the angle of incidence? T/I A

Electromagnetic Waves

Textbook pp. 538–539

MAIN IDEA: Electromagnetic waves have many applications. Photoelastic plastic uses polarized light to analyze stress patterns in a material subjected to varying loads. Lidar uses a laser to remotely sense properties of an object of interest from a distance.

1. Photoelastic materials
   (a) include glass and Lucite
   (b) have different indices of refraction for different polarizations of light
   (c) show stress patterns when placed between a polarizer and an analyzer
   (d) all of the above K/U

2. Photoelastic stress analysis
   (a) is performed on real structures
   (b) is used by engineers to determine areas where stress is concentrated in a material
   (c) is applied after the design is completed
   (d) all of the above K/U

3. Lidar can send a laser beam into the atmosphere. Scattered light from the particles of the atmosphere can be used to determine
   (a) air density
   (b) pressure
   (c) temperature
   (d) all of the above K/U

4. Indicate whether the following statements are true or false. If you think the statement is false, rewrite it to make it true. K/U

   (a) Photoelastic stress analysis can be performed on models undergoing tension or compression.

   (b) Lidar can determine the carbon dioxide concentration in the atmosphere.

STUDY TIP

Work with Others
Work in pairs or small groups to test your understanding of concepts.

Textbook pp. 540–541

Light Nanotechnology and Counterfeit Prevention

MAIN IDEA: Holography uses interference among light waves reflecting various points on an illuminated object to create a three-dimensional image of the object. Holography can be used for anti-counterfeiting schemes on bank notes, passports, and other documents. Nanotechnology uses tiny perforations to create colours without the use of inks. Reflection and refraction from these perforations result in unique colours that are currently impossible to duplicate.

1. A hologram
   (a) can be created using any source of light, such as white light from a light bulb
   (b) can only be created using a laser
   (c) always results in a fuzzy image
   (d) was invented by Clint Landrock in 1947 **K/U**

2. To produce a clear three-dimensional image in a hologram,
   (a) light from a laser is split into two beams before reaching the film
   (b) the hologram must be illuminated using a shorter wavelength laser light than the laser that created the image on the film
   (c) a photographer can use white light to form the image
   (d) all of the above **K/U**

3. An anti-counterfeiting mark on a bank note is made by drilling tiny holes into metal. A counterfeiter
   (a) can buy an expensive printer to replicate the mark
   (b) cannot duplicate the mark using current technology
   (c) can scan the mark to determine the pattern of the holes
   (d) can reproduce the mark using a powerful laser **K/U**

4. Indicate whether the following statements are true or false. If you think a statement is false, rewrite it to make it true. **K/U**

   (a) As a security measure for important documents such as bank notes, holograms are no longer secure, since the technology exists for counterfeiters to duplicate the holograms.

   (b) The colour of an insect such as a blue morpho butterfly is formed by reflection and refraction of light from tiny perforations in the wings.

Global Positioning Systems

Textbook pp. 542–543

MAIN IDEA: Global Positioning Systems (GPS) use electromagnetic signals from satellites orbiting Earth to determine position accurately in three-dimensions.

1. GPS was originally developed for
   (a) use by farmers to measure crop output
   (b) law enforcement
   (c) creating accurate maps
   (d) the military for tracking ships and submarines K/U

2. Drivers of automobiles who use GPS for navigation
   (a) may improve the acuity of memory and recall
   (b) are twice as likely to lose concentration while driving
   (c) may apply for reduced insurance premiums
   (d) all of the above K/U A

3. GPS measurements
   (a) are always accurate
   (b) are more accurate in areas with tall buildings
   (c) may lose accuracy if made under a canopy of trees
   (d) are not accurate enough for surveying applications K/U

4. Describe three applications of GPS technology. K/U

5. Is the following statement true or false? If you think the statement is false, rewrite it to make it true: Some insurance companies have linked GPS use to an increased number of traffic accidents. K/U

Applications of the Wave Nature of Light

Use the graphic organizer below to summarize what you have learned about applications of the wave nature of light. Connect the concepts. You can add your own notes, diagrams, and equations to this graphic organizer, creating a study tool to help you review Chapter 10.

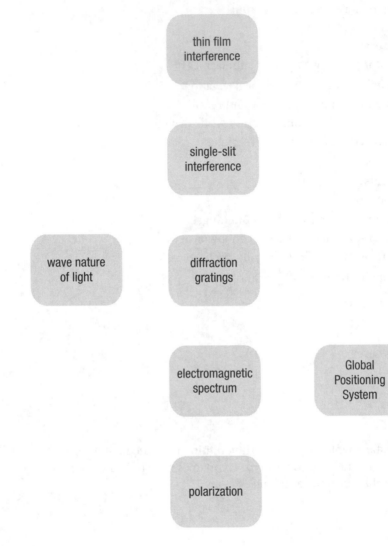

1. The colours reflected from soap bubbles are
   (a) caused by dispersion
   (b) a result of thin-film interference
   (c) a result of the very high index of refraction of soap
   (d) a result of long soap molecules forming a diffraction grating (10.1) K/U

2. A spectrometer measures wavelengths of light using
   (a) a diffraction grating
   (b) an air wedge
   (c) a polarizer
   (d) an analyzer (10.3) K/U

3. Indicate whether each statement is true or false. If you think the statement is false, rewrite it to make it true. K/U
   (a) The dark bands in a single-slit diffraction pattern are evenly spaced, except for the bands on either side of the centre line. These bands are spaced four times as widely as the others. (10.2)

   (b) The existence of electromagnetic waves was first confirmed experimentally by Hertz in his experiments with radio waves. (10.4)

4. Light with a wavelength of 610 nm illuminates a single slit with a width of 11.5 μm. A diffraction pattern appears 0.90 m behind the slit. What is the location of the second dark band after the central maximum? (10.2) K/U T/I A

K/U Knowledge/Understanding
T/I Thinking/Investigation
C   Communication
A   Application

5. A diffraction grating has 5400 lines/cm. It is illuminated with light with a wavelength of 480 nm. What is the angle at which the second-order bright band occurs? (10.3) T/I A

6. The first commercial broadcast television station in the Very High Frequency (VHF) band was on channel 2 at an assigned frequency of 54.0 MHz. The last channel assigned in the VHF range was channel 13, with a frequency of 210 MHz. How does the energy required by channel 13 compare to the energy required by channel 2 to broadcast at their assigned frequencies? (10.5) T/I A

7. A ray of light is sent through a polarizer and 35.0 % of the original intensity is transmitted. What is the angle between the polarizing axis of the polarizer and the polarization of the incident ray? (10.5) T/I A

8. Discuss two applications of the wave nature of light you learned about in this chapter. (10.6, 10.7, 10.8) K/U C

1. A periodic wave
   (a) is a moving disturbance that transports energy from one place to another
   (b) is a moving disturbance that transports matter from one place to another
   (c) never repeats itself
   (d) is the most complex wave possible (9.1) K/U

2. An unpolarized light ray travelling in air is incident on a polycarbonate surface at Brewster's angle. Which of the statements below is true? (10.5) K/U A
   (a) The reflected ray is perpendicular to the refracted ray.
   (b) The reflected ray is completely polarized.
   (c) The refracted ray is slightly polarized.
   (d) All of the above are true.

3. Indicate whether each statement is true or false. If you think the statement is false, rewrite it to make it true. K/U
   (a) Snell's law of refraction can be correctly derived using Huygens' principle. (9.4)

   (b) Since X-rays have a shorter wavelength than visible light, they travel through a vacuum at a slower speed than visible light. (10.4)

4. A ray of light travels from an unidentified transparent material into air with an angle of incidence of $32.0°$ and an angle of refraction of $53.1°$. Determine the index of refraction of the transparent material. (9.2) T/I A

K/U Knowledge/Understanding
T/I Thinking/Investigation
C   Communication
A   Application

5. Two slits are separated by a distance of 6.10×10^{-6} m and illuminated with a monochromatic light with a wavelength of 590 nm. What is the angle for the second-order dark fringe? (9.5) T/I A

6. A thin layer of liquid bromine with an index of refraction of $n = 1.66$ has coated a glass plate to a thickness of 90.4 nm. The index of refraction for the glass is 1.50. When illuminated with white light, the bromine appears orange in colour. What is the wavelength of the reflected light? (10.1) T/I A

7. A monochromatic light source with a wavelength of 520 nm illuminates a single slit with a width of 7.54 μm. What is the angle between the fourth bright band and the central maximum? (10.2) T/I A

Revolutions in Modern Physics: Quantum Mechanics and Special Relativity

Chapter 11: Relativity

A frame of reference is a coordinate system in which we can observe and measure the motion of an object. A frame of reference that moves with a constant velocity is an inertial frame of reference. The principle of relativity states that the laws of physics should be the same in all inertial frames of reference. The speed of light is the same in all inertial frames of reference.

An observer in an inertial reference frame will see the time in another inertial reference frame as running more slowly. An observer in an inertial reference frame will see the length of an object in another inertial reference frame as shortened along the direction of the relative velocity of the frame.

An observer in an inertial reference frame will see the momentum of an object in another inertial reference frame as greater than the classical momentum of the object.

An object with a mass m has a rest energy given by $E_{rest} = mc^2$. Mass and energy are equivalent.

Chapter 12: Quantum Mechanics

Many models in classical physics break down when applied to extremely small objects such as atoms. In the quantum world, all objects, including electromagnetic radiation and electrons, can exhibit interference and transfer energy in discrete amounts called quanta.

Wave-particle duality is the property of matter that defines its wave-like and particle-like characteristics. Wave-particle duality has many technological applications, such as electron microscopy and PET scans.

The work function is the minimum energy needed to remove an electron bound to a metal surface.

A photon is a quantum of electromagnetic energy. Photons have both energy and momentum, but no rest mass.

Planck's constant is a universal constant.

In the photoelectric effect, electrons are ejected when light strikes a metal. Energy is conserved. In the Compton effect, electrons are ejected along with a photon of lower energy when a photon strikes a metal. Energy and momentum are conserved.

Blackbody radiation can be explained by assuming that the energy in a blackbody comes in discrete parcels called quanta.

An electron possesses both particle-like and wave-like properties, including a wavelength related to its momentum. Electrons can produce an interference pattern when aimed at a crystal.

A wave function gives the probability for any quantum object to take any possible path, or for the object to be at any possible location.

The Heisenberg uncertainty principle says that we cannot determine both the position and momentum of a given object with great accuracy.

BIG IDEAS

- Light can show particle-like and wave-like behaviour, and particles can show wave-like behaviour.

- The behaviour of light as a particle and the behaviour of particles as waves can be described mathematically.

- Time is relative to a person's frame of reference.

- The effects of relativistic motion can be described mathematically.

- New theories can change scientific thought and lead to the development of new technologies.

The Special Theory of Relativity

Textbook pp. 574–579

Vocabulary

frame of reference   ether   postulate

inertial frame of reference   thought experiment   special theory of relativity

principle of relativity

MAIN IDEA: A frame of reference that moves with a constant velocity is one in which the law of inertia holds, or an inertial frame of reference. The principle of relativity states that the laws of physics should be the same in all inertial frames of reference. The ether was a hypothetical medium through which electromagnetic waves propagated. Tests such as the Michelson-Morley experiment failed to verify that an ether actually existed.

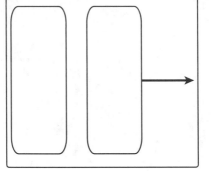
1. At the turn of the twentieth century, what problem remained unexplained according to physicists at the time? K/U
   (a) All problems had been explained.
   (b) how to unify the concepts of electricity and magnetism
   (c) the nature of light
   (d) the observed radiation from blackbodies

2. Alexa is standing in a railroad car moving east at 80 km/h. She tosses a ball with an initial velocity of 15 km/h [up] relative to the car. When the ball comes back down, where will it land, relative to Alexa? Explain your answer. K/U T/I
   (a) east of Alexa   (c) above Alexa
   (b) west of Alexa   (d) north of Alexa

3. An airline passenger is walking on a moving sidewalk at 1.50 m/s [E] relative to the sidewalk. The sidewalk is moving at 1.80 m/s [E] relative to the airport terminal. He tosses a ball back toward a friend standing on the sidewalk behind him at a speed of 1.30 m/s relative to himself. Determine the velocity of the ball relative to the airport terminal. T/I A

4. A thought experiment
   (a) is a mental exercise
   (b) examines possible flaws in a hypothesis
   (c) is useful when a real experiment is impractical
   (d) all of the above K/U

MAIN IDEA: Einstein's theory of relativity is based on two postulates: (a) all the laws of physics are the same in all inertial frames of reference, and (b) in at least one inertial frame of reference the speed of light is independent of the motion of the source of the light. One result of Einstein's postulates is the statement that the speed of light is the same in all inertial frames of reference, regardless of their velocity.

5. Gus brings a cart and spring scale onto a school bus, which is parked in a parking lot. He finds that the cart requires a force of 2.00 N to accelerate it north at 1.00 m/s². The bus accelerates north at 2.00 m/s² until it reaches a speed of 8.00 m/s, and then maintains a constant velocity. Gus uses the spring scale to accelerate the cart to the north at 1.00 m/s². What is the force required? Explain your answer. K/U T/I

   (a) 1.00 N
   (b) 2.00 N
   (c) 3.00 N
   (d) 4.00 N

6. Why may we consider the surface of Earth to be an inertial frame of reference? K/U

   (a) Earth is at rest with respect to the Sun.
   (b) The solar system is at rest with respect to the galaxy.
   (c) The accelerations due to planetary motion are very small.
   (d) all of the above

7. The spacecrafts Alpha and Bravo are 3.00×10^8 m apart and moving directly toward each other along a straight line. The speed of each spacecraft is $0.5c$, as measured by a stationary observer. Alpha sends a message to Bravo via laser beam. How long does it take for the message to reach Bravo, from the frame of reference of the stationary observer? Explain your answer. T/I A

   (a) 2.00 s
   (b) 1.00 s
   (c) 0.50 s
   (d) 0.25 s

8. Is the following statement true or false? If you think the statement is false, rewrite it to make it true: The existence of the luminiferous ether was postulated because it was thought that electromagnetic waves needed a medium through which to travel. K/U

Time Dilation

Textbook pp. 580–587

Vocabulary

time dilation   relativistic time   proper time (Δt_s)

MAIN IDEA: An observer in an inertial reference frame will see the time in another inertial reference frame as running slower. The equation for time dilation is $\Delta t_m = \dfrac{\Delta t_s}{\sqrt{1 - \dfrac{v^2}{c^2}}}$.

The value $\sqrt{1 - \dfrac{v^2}{c^2}}$ is undefined for v greater than c.

STUDY **TIP**

Use a Graphic Organizer
Time dilation, along with other relativistic effects, can be confusing. Use the graphic organizer suggested in section 11.1 to keep observer and observed phenomenon clear in your mind. Relativistic effects often seem counter-intuitive.

1. You are observer A and you are holding clock A. Observer B passes you, holding clock B and moving at a constant velocity. Select the best statement from the options below. Explain your answer. K/U C

   (a) You see clock A running normally, but clock B running slowly.

   (b) Observer B sees clock B running normally, but clock A running slowly.

   (c) You see clock B running slowly, and observer B sees clock A running faster than normal.

   (d) Both (a) and (b) are true.

2. A pendulum on a spacecraft swings with a period of 2.5 s in the frame of reference of the spacecraft. If the ship is moving at 0.99c, how long is the period from the perspective of a stationary observer? T/I A

3. A chess game is taking place on a spacecraft moving with a constant velocity relative to you, at a speed of 0.75c. From your frame of reference on Earth, the game lasts 90 min. How long does the game last from the point of view of the players? T/I A

4. A spacecraft passes a space station. Observers on the station see a clock on the spacecraft. The minute hand appears to take 100 s to complete a cycle. How fast is the spacecraft moving relative to the space station? T/I A

MAIN IDEA: Time dilation is a natural result of the two postulates of special relativity and the realization that the speed of light is the same for all observers. Numerous experiments have provided evidence of time dilation, including the Hafele-Keating experiment using passenger jets and atomic clocks. Time dilation, along with other general relativity corrections, is used to maintain the accuracy of GPS systems.

5. Atomic clocks of the 1970s were accurate enough to measure time dilation effects. However, there are other complications in testing Einstein's theory. What are some of these complications? K/U T/I

6. Is the following statement true or false? If you think the statement is false, rewrite it to make it true: Einstein's theory of relativity was readily accepted by physicists in 1905 because the technology to test the theory experimentally was available. K/U

Length Contraction, Simultaneity, and Relativistic Momentum

> **Vocabulary**
>
> | | | |
> |---|---|---|
> | proper length (L_s) | simultaneity | relativistic momentum |
> | length contraction | twin paradox | rest mass |
> | relativistic length (L_m) | space-time | relativistic mass |

MAIN IDEA: Proper length, L_s, is the length of an object as measured by an observer who is at rest with respect to the object. Relativistic length, L_m, is the length of the object as measured by an observer not at rest with respect to the object. The equation for length contraction is $L_m = L_s\sqrt{1 - \dfrac{v^2}{c^2}}$. Contraction occurs along the direction of motion. For two observers in motion relative to each other, events that appear simultaneous for one observer are not simultaneous for the other observer. However, in both cases, events appear to both observers in the order that they occur. The observers perceive the time between the two events differently.

1. When must special relativity must be taken into account? K/U
   (a) for aircraft flying near the speed of sound
   (b) for cars driving on a superhighway
   (c) when operating a particle accelerator
   (d) all of the above

2. A comic book hero has a height of 1.78 m in his rest frame. He flies horizontally at 0.25c. How does the length of his body appear to an observer at rest? T/I A

3. Points A, B, C, D, and E are evenly spaced, in order, along a line. A is set moving away from B at a constant velocity, and E is set moving away from D at a constant velocity. Both remain on the original straight line. Lights at B and D are turned on simultaneously as determined by an observer at C. Which statement is true? K/U T/I A
   (a) An observer moving with A will see B light up before D.
   (b) An observer moving with E will see D light up before B.
   (c) Both (a) and (b) are true.
   (d) Observers, A, C, and E, will see B and D light up simultaneously.

MAIN IDEA: The equation for relativistic momentum is $p = \dfrac{mv}{\sqrt{1 - \dfrac{v^2}{c^2}}}$ Relativistic momentum increases as the speed increases and is limited by the speed of light. The rest mass of an object is the mass of the object as measured by an observer at rest with respect to the object. No object with a rest mass greater than zero can move as fast as, or faster than, the speed of light.

4. A spacecraft is moving with a speed of $0.90c$. How does its relativistic momentum compare with its classical momentum? T/I A

5. Cosmic ray protons that strike Earth's atmosphere appear to have a momentum of 1.11 times that expected of classical particles. At what speed are the protons moving? T/I A

11.3 Length Contraction, Simultaneity, and Relativistic Momentum

Mass–Energy Equivalence

> **Vocabulary**
>
> rest energy (E_{rest})   relativistic kinetic energy (E_k)   conservation of mass–energy

MAIN IDEA: The rest energy of an object with mass m is the amount of energy the object has when at rest with respect to an observer. It is a measure of the energy that is intrinsically contained in the matter that makes up the object and is given by the equation $E_{rest} = mc^2$.

1. Is the following statement true or false? If you think the statement is false, rewrite it to make it true: A car moving at 100 km/h has a greater mass than the same car at rest. K/U

2. Gasoline contains about 47.2 MJ of energy per 1.00 kg when burned. Suppose that a car could convert this mass directly to energy. How many times farther could the car be driven on this energy, compared to the energy given off when burned? T/I A

STUDY TIP

Reasonableness of Answers
Check the reasonableness of your answers. For example, is the velocity of an object less than the speed of light?

3. A linear accelerator accelerates electrons a distance of 3.12 m. Each electron acquires a relativistic mass 7.09 times its rest mass. What is the speed of each electron? T/I A

MAIN IDEA: The total relativistic energy of an object with rest mass m is $E_{total} = \dfrac{mc^2}{\sqrt{1 - \dfrac{v^2}{c^2}}}$.

This expression is equal to the sum of the kinetic energy and the rest energy of the object: $E_{total} = E_{rest} + E_k$. Special relativity shows that mass and energy are equivalent, and thus establishes the principle of conservation of mass–energy. The energy produced from nuclear reactions has many applications, including nuclear power and nuclear weapons.

4. A light photon has a total energy of 2.00 eV. What is its rest energy? Explain your answer. K/U
   - (a) 4.00 eV
   - (b) 2.00 eV
   - (c) 1.00 eV
   - (d) 0 eV

5. Mass–energy conversion occurs in many physical and chemical processes. Give three examples of such processes. T/I A

6. A medical linear accelerator produces electrons with a total energy of 30.0 MeV. These are directed onto a metallic target to produce a beam of X-rays used to treat some forms of cancer. The mass of an electron is 9.11×10^{-31} kg. What is the speed of an electron when it leaves the accelerator? T/I A

Relativity

Use the graphic organizer below to summarize what you have learned about relativity. You can add your own notes, diagrams, and equations to this graphic organizer, creating a study tool to help you review Chapter 11.

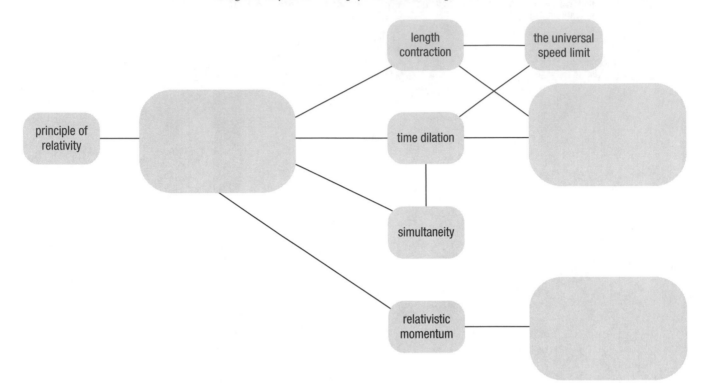

principle of relativity

length contraction

the universal speed limit

time dilation

simultaneity

relativistic momentum

1. GPS navigation devices
    (a) do not need to take time dilation into account since the satellites move very slowly
    (b) are not affected by the gravity of Earth
    (c) are accurate to approximately 15 m
    (d) all of the above (11.2) K/U

2. A metre stick is thrown past you at a speed of 0.50c in a direction along its length. From your frame of reference the stick appears to be what length? (11.3) K/U
    (a) 1.00 m long
    (b) less than 1.00 m but more than 0.50 m long
    (c) exactly 0.50 m long
    (d) less than 0.50 m but more than 0 m long

3. Indicate whether each statement is true or false. If you think the statement is false, rewrite it to make it true. K/U
    (a) An accelerating frame of reference can be considered a non-inertial frame of reference. (11.1)

    (b) Mass–energy equivalence applies only to subatomic particles such as electrons or protons and not to ordinary objects like baseballs. (11.4)

4. A spacecraft travelling at 0.975c passes your spacecraft. You see a crewmember on the ship drink a glass of water in 12.4 s. How long did the drink last from the frame of reference of the crewmember? (11.2) T/I A

K/U Knowledge/Understanding
T/I Thinking/Investigation
C Communication
A Application

5. Earth has a diameter of approximately 1.28×10^4 km. A spacecraft flies away from Earth at a speed of $0.920c$. An astronaut on the ship measures the diameter of Earth along the direction of flight of the ship. What does the diameter appear to be from the astronaut's frame of reference? (11.3) T/I A

6. Jan drove her car such that the relativistic momentum appeared to be 2.00 times the expected classical momentum to a stationary observer. At what speed was the car travelling? (11.3) T/I A

7. When a uranium-235 nucleus fissions in a nuclear reactor, it releases, on average, approximately 202 MeV of thermal energy. How much of the original mass of the uranium nucleus is converted into thermal energy? (11.4) T/I A

Introducing Quantum Theory

> **Vocabulary**
>
> quantum   quantum theory   wave–particle duality

Textbook pp. 616–619

MAIN IDEA: The quantum world is the world of subatomic particles and their behaviours. Many models in classical physics break down when applied to extremely small objects such as atoms. In classical physics, energy can be carried from one point to another in the form of either waves or particles. In classical physics, waves exhibit interference; particles do not. Particles often deliver their energy in discrete amounts but waves do not. In the quantum world, all objects, including electromagnetic radiation and electrons, can exhibit interference and transfer energy in discrete amounts called quanta.

1. Classical physics does not apply to the motion of which object? K/U
   (a) a baseball in a microgravity environment
   (b) a spaceship far from any star or large planetary body
   (c) an electron in an electron microscope
   (d) all of the above

2. The "quantum" in "quantum theory" refers to a small unit of which of the following? K/U
   (a) energy   (c) momentum
   (b) mass   (d) speed

3. Which of these carry energy from one place to another? K/U
   (a) sound from a loudspeaker
   (b) light from a fluorescent lamp
   (c) a golf ball driven from a tee to the fairway
   (d) all of the above

> **LEARNING TIP**
>
> **Quantum Theory**
> Do not be alarmed if quantum theory seems to go against common sense. Many physicists thought that the counter-intuitiveness of quantum mechanics would disappear once a more fundamental underlying theory came to light. So far, it has not, and all experiments have supported the strange behaviour of subatomic particles and processes.

MAIN IDEA: Wave–particle duality is the property of matter that defines its wave-like and particle-like characteristics.

4. Interference effects can be seen with electrons passing through two slits with as few as _____ electron(s). K/U
   (a) 10 000
   (b) 200
   (c) 1
   (d) Electrons are particles and show no interference effects.

5. In classical physics, the energy carried by a wave is described by which of the following? K/U
   (a) intensity   (c) frequency
   (b) wavelength   (d) phase

6. Is the following statement true or false? If you think the statement is false, rewrite it to make it true: Particles can carry energy in discrete quantities, but waves cannot. K/U

7. **Figure 1** shows an experimental setup to investigate the behaviour of electrons passing through two slits. K/U C

   (a) Place the labels in the correct places on Figure 1:

   electrons

   double slit

   recording screen

   (b) The screen records where electrons strike the screen. Sketch a pattern on the diagram that represents the probability that an electron will strike the screen.

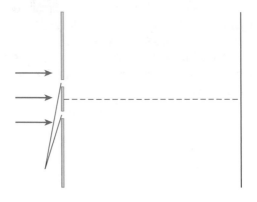

Figure 1

8. Two tennis balls are thrown toward two slits. The tennis balls leave marks on a wall after passing through the slits. **Figure 2** shows the distribution of tennis-ball marks made on the wall when each slit is open. On **Figure 3**, draw the distribution pattern you would expect to see if both slit 1 and slit 2 were open at the same time. Explain your answer. K/U C

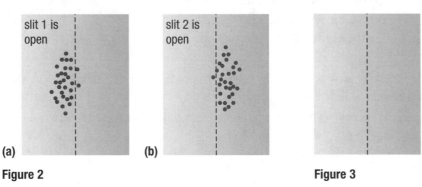

(a)

Figure 2

Figure 3

Photons and the Quantum Theory of Light

Vocabulary

work function (W)	photon	pair creation
photoelectric effect	Planck's constant (h)	blackbody
threshold frequency (f_0)	Compton effect	blackbody radiation

MAIN IDEA: The work function, W, is the minimum energy needed to remove an electron bound to a metal surface. The work function equation is $W = e\Delta V$. A photon is a quantum of electromagnetic energy. The quantum theory of light says that photons have both energy, $E = hf$, and momentum, $p = \dfrac{hf}{c} = \dfrac{h}{\lambda}$. Planck's constant, h, is a universal constant with a value of approximately 6.63×10^{-34} J·s.

1. A red light shining on a metal surface fails to produce photoelectrons. According to Einstein, what should be done to produce photoelectrons? K/U
   (a) Increase the intensity of the red light.
   (b) Decrease the intensity of the red light.
   (c) Increase the frequency of the light towards the violet.
   (d) Decrease the frequency of the light towards the infrared.

2. Platinum has a work function of 5.64 eV. What is the minimum photon frequency necessary to eject electrons from a platinum-coated surface in a vacuum tube? T/I A

3. A cordless telephone operates at a frequency of 5.8 GHz. Determine the energy and momentum of a photon produced by the telephone when it is in operation. T/I A

> **STUDY TIP**
>
> **Conversion Charts**
> List the conversion factors for units of measurement in a table or chart for quick reference.

MAIN IDEA: In the photoelectric effect, photons are ejected when light strikes a metal. Energy is conserved during this process. In the Compton effect, electrons are ejected when X-rays strike a metal. Energy and momentum are conserved during this process. Planck explained the observed spectrum of blackbody radiation by assuming the energy in a blackbody comes in discrete parcels called quanta. The photoelectric effect and blackbody radiation demonstrate that photons exhibit both wave-like and particle-like properties.

4. Fill in the blanks with the correct terms. K/U

   The Compton effect is a process that conserves _____

   and _____. Classical physics does not explain the

   experimental results properly, and the Compton effect must be analyzed using

   the equations of _____.

5. What is true about a blackbody? K/U
   (a) It absorbs only visible light radiation.
   (b) It cannot emit radiation of its own.
   (c) It appears the colour of the wavelength of the maximum radiation intensity.
   (d) all of the above

6. Is the following statement true or false? If you think the statement is false, rewrite it to make it true: The energy of a photon can be converted to particles with mass in some interactions. K/U

7. The maximum intensity of a blackbody occurs at green light of about 520 nm. What is the temperature of the blackbody? T/I A

Wave Properties of Classical Particles

Textbook pp. 632–639

Vocabulary

de Broglie wavelength   matter wave   Heisenberg uncertainty principle

MAIN IDEA: Louis de Broglie hypothesized that electrons possess both particle-like and wave-like properties, including a wavelength related to their momentum as $\lambda = \dfrac{h}{p}$. Experiments by Davisson and Germer confirmed that electrons exhibit the wave-like property of interference in accordance with de Broglie's wavelength. The equations of quantum mechanics do not explain what happens to a single electron during a double-slit experiment. Different interpretations include the collapse interpretation, the pilot wave interpretation, the many worlds interpretation, and the Copenhagen interpretation. A wave function gives the probability for any quantum object to take any possible path or to be at any possible location on the detection screen.

1. De Broglie hypothesized that particles have wave-like properties. What is a key feature of this hypothesis? Explain your answer. K/U T/I
   - (a) It applies only to subatomic particles like electrons and protons.
   - (b) It correctly explains the results when electrons are sent through a crystal onto a screen.
   - (c) It predicts an increase in wavelength as momentum increases.
   - (d) all of the above

2. A proton has a mass of 1.67×10^{-27} kg. It is accelerated to an energy of 100.0 MeV in a linear accelerator. What is the proton's de Broglie wavelength on leaving the accelerator? T/I A

3. A student decides to demonstrate interference using tennis balls that she will throw at a pair of slits cut into a sheet of wood. Each ball has a mass of 57.0 g and will be moving at 20.0 m/s. What approximate slit separation should the student use to produce an interference pattern? Explain any problems in performing this experiment. T/I A

> **LEARNING TIP**
>
> **Lucky Discoveries**
> Accidents sometimes lead to important discoveries. Davisson and Germer were not looking for evidence of electron diffraction. They were studying the surface of nickel by analyzing how it reflected a beam of electrons. They were expecting diffuse reflection and were surprised to see a diffraction pattern.

MAIN IDEA: The Heisenberg uncertainty principle states that we cannot simultaneously determine the position and momentum of a quantum object. Wave-particle duality has many technological applications, such as electron microscopy and PET scans.

4. According to the _____ interpretation of quantum mechanics, some questions do not have answers, such as how an electron beam can produce an interference pattern. K/U

    (a) collapse

    (b) pilot wave

    (c) many worlds

    (d) Copenhagen

5. Which of the following statements is true of wave–particle duality? K/U

    (a) It applies only to subatomic processes such as radioactivity or nuclear fission.

    (b) It makes electronic devices such as cell phones and computers possible.

    (c) It applies only to charged particles such as electrons, protons, or positrons.

    (d) It is not applicable to the operation of an electron microscope.

6. The Heisenberg uncertainty principle states which of the following? K/U

    (a) If you measure the position of a quantum object with great accuracy, then you can only measure its momentum with little accuracy.

    (b) If you measure the position of a quantum object with great accuracy, then you can also measure its momentum with great accuracy.

    (c) If you measure the position of a quantum object, then the system remains undisturbed.

    (d) none of the above

7. The spacing in molybdenum crystals used in an electron diffraction experiment is about 7.11 nm. Take this to be the uncertainty in the position of an electron. What is the uncertainty in its momentum? T/I A

Medical Diagnostic Tools

Textbook pp. 640–641

MAIN IDEA: Quantum mechanics has led to the development of many medical diagnostic tools such as PET scans and electron microscopes.

1. Which of the following do PET scans measure? K/U
   (a) blood flow
   (b) oxygen use
   (c) sugar metabolism
   (d) all of the above

2. A positron is the antimatter analogue of an electron. It has the same mass, but carries a positive charge. Positrons are needed for the operation of which diagnostic tool? K/U
   (a) an electron microscope
   (b) PET scans
   (c) CT scans
   (d) all of the above

3. Brain waves can be used to produce operating instructions for artificial limbs using which technology? K/U
   (a) electron microscope
   (b) SQUID
   (c) CT machine
   (d) positron-emitting materials

4. Which diagnostic tool is a non-invasive method of producing medical images? K/U
   (a) PET scan
   (b) laser
   (c) electron microscope
   (d) all of the above

5. Is the following statement true or false? If you think the statement is false, rewrite it to make it true: The transfer of electrons during light absorption in the process of photosynthesis takes place using classical physical processes. K/U

Physics JOURNAL

Textbook pp. 642–643

Raymond Laflamme and Quantum Information Theory

MAIN IDEA: Quantum computers can store much more information than classical computers and manipulate the information much faster. Classical computers rely on the binary system of 0s and 1s, while quantum computers can also use superpositions of 0 and 1. Information can be encoded using the polarization of the photons carrying the information.

1. Which statement about Raymond Laflamme is true? K/U
   (a) He studied under Albert Einstein.
   (b) He is a Canadian from the province of Quebec.
   (c) He currently works for NASA.
   (d) all of the above

2. Which statement about a qubit is true? K/U
   (a) It can be made from a single atom.
   (b) It has a value of either 0 or 1.
   (c) It is the basic unit of memory on a classical computer.
   (d) all of the above

3. Which statement about errors in quantum computers is true? K/U
   (a) Errors cannot occur.
   (b) Errors may be the result of decoherence.
   (c) Errors can be corrected using a large number as an encryption key.
   (d) Errors cannot be corrected since they are quantum systems subject to Heisenberg's uncertainty principle.

4. Fill in the blanks with the words provided.

   passwords   decoding   Internet   secure   encoding

   Cryptography is the science of _____ and _____ information. It is used to encode _____ before they are transmitted over the _____ so that a third party cannot read _____ information. K/U

5. Indicate whether each statement is true or false. If you think the statement is false, rewrite it to make it true. K/U
   (a) An encryption key is based on a large number that cannot be decoded by a quantum computer.

   (b) An electronic eavesdropper can intercept an encrypted message, determine the polarization key, and then send the message onwards without being detected.

The Standard Model of Elementary Particles

Textbook pp. 644–653

Vocabulary		
antimatter	standard model	gluon
quark	fermions	Higgs boson
hadrons	boson	theory of everything
leptons		

MAIN IDEA: Rutherford discovered the nucleus and proposed that electrons in an atom orbit the nucleus like a planetary system. Classical physics predicts that this system is not stable. The Bohr model of the atom proposes that electrons can only orbit the nucleus at certain allowed energy levels. These electrons transition between levels by emitting or absorbing photons whose energies are equal to the difference between the energy levels.

1. What was Ernest Rutherford's contribution to our understanding of the atom? K/U
   (a) He determined his model of the atom by aiming electrons at a thin sheet of gold foil.
   (b) He explained the deflection of some particles by assuming that most of the positive charge in an atom is concentrated in a small space.
   (c) He suggested that protons in an atom orbit the nucleus like the planets orbit the Sun.
   (d) all of the above

2. Which of the following statements is true about protons in the nucleus of an atom? K/U
   (a) They should fly apart due to electrostatic repulsion.
   (b) They are held together by the strong nuclear force.
   (c) They need neutrons to contribute to the strong nuclear force without adding to electrostatic repulsion.
   (d) all of the above

3. What is true about the planetary model of the atom? K/U
   (a) It is still the model used today.
   (b) It was successfully modified to explain why electron orbits do not decay.
   (c) It leads to instability since electrons in a circular orbit should radiate energy.
   (d) It was confirmed by Neils Bohr.

4. Summarize three of the key features of the Bohr model of the atom that are different from the Rutherford model. K/U

MAIN IDEA: Antimatter is a particle of matter that has the same mass but opposite charge as its corresponding particle of ordinary matter. The positron is the antimatter version of the electron. All particles in the universe interact through three fundamental forces of nature.

5. What is true about antimatter? K/U
   (a) It was predicted by the quantum theory of Dirac.
   (b) It has not yet been verified experimentally.
   (c) It includes protons and electrons.
   (d) It does not have an analogue for a neutron, since a neutron has no charge.

6. When an electron and positron meet they annihilate each other. What is the result? K/U
   (a) Only energy is conserved in the interaction.
   (b) Only momentum is conserved in the interaction.
   (c) The energy of the gamma rays produced equals the sum of the rest and kinetic energies of the electron and positron.
   (d) all of the above

MAIN IDEA: The standard model is the current theory of particle physics, which predicts that nature consists of quarks, leptons, and bosons that interact through fundamental forces. Quarks combine to form hadrons. Leptons are elementary particles, and include electrons and neutrinos. Bosons mediate fundamental forces. The Higgs boson helps explain the origin of the mass of other fundamental particles. A theory of everything attempts to explain and predict interactions in both the macroscopic and quantum worlds by combining quantum mechanics and general relativity into one theory.

7. Which of these is a hadron? K/U
   (a) neutron   (c) quark
   (b) positron   (d) all of the above

8. Label **Figure 1** with the appropriate quark representation of a baryon (proton, neutron, anti-proton). K/U

Figure 1

9. What is true about quarks? K/U
   (a) They occur in six flavours.
   (b) They combine to make up hadrons.
   (c) They can combine with anti-quarks to make up other particles.
   (d) all of the above

10. What is true about neutrinos? K/U
    (a) They occur in four types.
    (b) They change type back and as they travel through space.
    (c) They are made up of two quarks.
    (d) all of the above

11. Experimental observation has succeeded for which particles? K/U
    (a) all particles in the standard model
    (b) all quarks, leptons, and bosons
    (c) all particles in the standard model except the Higgs boson
    (d) some quarks, some leptons, and some bosons

12. Is the following statement true or false? If you think the statement is false, rewrite it to make it true: A theory of everything must combine the strong and weak nuclear forces. K/U

Quantum Mechanics

Use the graphic organizer below to summarize what you have learned about quantum mechanics. Add lines to connect concepts. You can add your own notes, diagrams, and equations to this graphic organizer, creating a study tool to help you review Chapter 12.

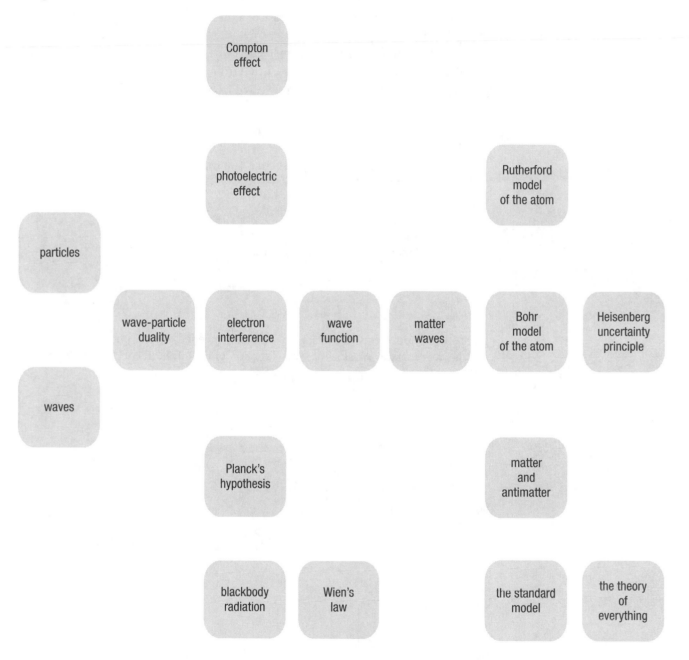

K/U   Knowledge/Understanding
T/I   Thinking/Investigation
C   Communication
A   Application

1. What are quanta? (12.1) K/U

   (a) discrete amounts of energy
   (b) units of momentum for subatomic particles
   (c) units of momentum for photons
   (d) electron masses

2. Compton directed a beam of X-rays at a metal surface. What did he detect? (12.2) K/U

   (a) electrons ejected from the metal surface
   (b) lower energy X-ray photons ejected from the metal surface
   (c) higher energy X-ray photons ejected from the metal surface
   (d) both (a) and (b)

3. Indicate whether each statement is true or false. If you think the statement is false, rewrite it to make it true. K/U

   (a) Quantum mechanics suggests that you may exist in different versions in different parallel worlds. (12.3)

   (b) Decoherence prevents errors in quantum computers. (12.5)

4. A minimum frequency of 1.12×10^{15} Hz is needed to eject photoelectrons from a silver surface. What is the work function of the silver, in eV? (12.2) T/I A

5. A medical X-ray machine operates at 30.0 petahertz, or 3.00×10^{16} Hz. Determine the energy and momentum of a photon from this machine. (12.2) T/I A

6. The surface temperature of the Sun is about 5800 K. How does the observed colour of the Sun compare with that of a blackbody at the same temperature? Explain your reasoning. (12.2) T/I A

7. An alpha particle ejected from a radioactive nucleus has a mass of 6.64×10^{-27} kg and an energy of 5.00 MeV. What is its de Broglie wavelength? (12.3) T/I A

8. List three medical diagnostic tools that apply quantum mechanics. (12.6) K/U

1. Which statement about the luminiferous ether is true? (11.1) K/U
   (a) It was detected by the Michelson-Morley experiment.
   (b) It was thought to have no mass.
   (c) It exerts a drag effect on the motion of planets.
   (d) all of the above

2. What is true about the Bohr model of the hydrogen atom? (12.6) K/U
   (a) It treats electron orbits as standing waves.
   (b) It makes use of de Broglie's equation.
   (c) It postulates an integral number of wavelengths for the circumference of the orbit.
   (d) all of the above

3. Indicate whether each statement is true or false. If you think the statement is false, rewrite it to make it true. K/U
   (a) Time dilation is an illusory effect resulting from the "constant speed of light for all observers" postulate of special relativity. (11.2)

   (b) Lasik eye surgery uses a beam of electrons to make incisions in the cornea for vision correction. (12.4)

4. A pole-vaulter is carrying a pole horizontally on her shoulder. She runs toward a small building that has a front and back door. The distance between the doors is half of the length of the pole. How fast must she run such that, at one instant, her pole appears to be entirely within the building, from the point of view of a stationary observer? (11.3) T/I A

5. A typical human requires about 5.45 MJ of energy per day. Assuming that humans could convert food directly into energy, what mass of food would meet one human's daily energy requirements? (11.4) T/I A

6. Iron has a work function of 7.48×10^{-19} J. Can visible light eject photoelectrons from iron? Provide numerical evidence. (12.2) T/I A

7. The Large Hadron Collider will accelerate protons to near the speed of light. The speed of the protons can be measured to an accuracy of 1 %. What is the uncertainty in the position of such a proton? Ignore the relativistic mass increase for this calculation. Assume that the mass of each proton is 1.67×10^{-27} kg. (12.3) T/I A

8. Briefly discuss what quantum crytography is in your own words. (12.5) K/U C

Answers

These pages include numerical and short answers to chapter section questions, Chapter Questions, and Unit Questions.

Unit 1

1.1, pp. 2–5
1. Figure 1: speed versus time; Figure 2: acceleration versus time
2. (a) 150 km/h
   (b) 150 km/h [E]
   (c) 160 km/h
   (d) 80 km/h [E]
3. (a) 25 m/s [E]
   (b) 19 m/s [E]
4. (a) -1.3 m/s^2 [N]
   (b) -3.0 m/s^2 [N]

1.2, pp. 6–7
1. 150 m [N]
2. -8.0 km/h^2 [W] or 8.0 km/h^2 [E]
3. 563 m [E]
4. $\Delta t = 10$ s
5. $\Delta t = 8.00$ s
6. 28.3 m/s [down]

1.3, pp. 8–9
1. c
2. T
3. (a) 120 km [W 55° N]
   (b) 120 km [W 55° N]
4. a
5. 11 km [E 20° S]
6. 18.7 km [W 12° S]

1.4, pp. 10–11
1. d
2. 4.1 km/h [W 23° N]
3. c
4. 77.1 km/h [E 70° N]
5. T
6. 400 km/h^2 [W 56° N]

1.5, pp. 12–13
1. c
2. d
3. 99.9 m
4. (a) 32.3 m/s
   (b) 13.3 m
5. 39.2 m
6. Christy
7. 7.17 m

1.6, pp. 14–15
1. yes
2. c
3. 329 km/h [S]
4. (a) 3.5 m/s [N]
   (b) 0.5 m/s [S]
   (c) 2.5 m/s [E 37° N]
5. [W 13° N]
6. [E 13° N]

Chapter 1 Questions, pp. 17–18
1. a
2. b

3. (a) F
   (b) F
   (c) T
   (d) T
4. -43 m/s [E] or 43 m/s [W]
5. -6.00 m/s^2 [S]
6. 7.2 km [E 6° S]
7. 97 km/h/s [E 31° N]
9. 10:30 a.m.

2.1, pp. 19–20
1. b
2. F
3. applied force, gravity, kinetic friction, air resistance
5. (c) 182.0 N [W]

2.2, pp. 21–22
1. no
2. no
4. 0.1 m/s^2 [forward]
5. 0.75 m/s^2 [E 3.0° S]
6. no
7. a
8. 588 N [down]

2.3, pp. 23–24
1. d
2. 116 N
3. 4.7×10^2 N
4. (b) 33.9 N
5. 6.11 N [W 77.0° up]

2.4, pp. 25–26
1. b
2. 79.0 N [backwards]
3. d
4. 57 g
5. accelerate down the hill

2.5, p. 27
1. c
2. d
3. (a) F
   (b) F

2.6, p. 28
1. a
2. F
3. b
4. d
5. a

Chapter 2 Questions, pp. 30–31
1. c
2. c
3. (a) F
   (b) F
   (c) T
   (d) T
4. 15.0 N [E]
5. 24.3 N [E 63.5° N]
6. 797 N [S 84.1° up]
7. 230 m [W]

3.1, pp. 32–33
1. (a) inertial
   (b) inertial
   (c) non-inertial
   (d) non-inertial
3. no
5. 2.7 m/s^2
6. 71.1°

3.2, pp. 34–35
1. d
2. F
4. 6.67 m/s^2
5. 0.809 m/s^2
6. 266 m/s^2

3.3, pp. 36–37
1. north
3. (a) T
   (b) T
   (c) F
4. 154 N
5. 21.5°

3.4, pp. 38–39
1. d
2. yes
3. c
4. 44.2 m/s
5. 4.93 m/s^2 or 0.503 g

3.5, p. 40
2. b
3. 40.8 m

3.6, p. 41
2. d

Chapter 3 Questions, pp. 43–44
1. d
2. b
3. (a) T
   (b) T
   (c) T
   (d) F
4. 1.59 m/s^2
5. 1340 m/s^2
6. (a) 491 N
7. 4.76 s
9. 10.8 m/s

Unit 1 Questions, pp. 45–46
1. d
2. a
3. b
4. (a) T
   (b) F
   (c) F
5. 3.76 m/s [W]
6. 22.6 m
7. 2.45 N
8. 127 m

9. 0 N
10. 88.5 m/s

Unit 2

4.1, pp. 48–50
3. newton-metre, joule
4. (a) A: iii; B: i; C: ii
   (b) ii
6. 2.4×10^2 J
7. -1.3×10^6 J
8. kinetic
9. all, friction
10. (b) 4.8×10^4 J
    (c) -3.02×10^4 J
    (d) 1.87×10^4 J
11. force, displacement, force, displacement

4.2, pp. 51–52
1. work, joules
3. scalar quantity
4. 2.48×10^3 kg
5. 2.3×10^2 J
6. 1.14 m/s
7. (a) no energy losses occur
   (b) no

4.3, p. 53–54
3. 0 J
4. floor of the second-floor balcony
5. 25 J
7. 3.44×10^5 J or 344 kJ
8. (a) 1.20×10^5 J
   (b) 3.7×10^2 kg

4.5, pp. 56–58
2. (a) 5.7×10^5 J
   (b) 1.5×10^5 J
   (c) gravity
5. $p = \dfrac{\Delta E_k}{t}$
6. joule, watt, kJ, second
7. 7.4×10^3 W or 7.4 kW

4.6, pp. 59–61
1. (a) (i) stretched
   (b) (ii) equilibrium position
       (iii) compressed
2. (a) left
   (b) right
3. no
5. (a) F
   (b) T
   (c) F
7. 1.7 m [down]
8. 62.5 J
9. 5.2 J
11. 16 kg; 0.25 Hz

4.7, pp. 62–63
1. 9.0 cm

Chapter 4 Questions, pp. 65–66

1. c
2. a
3. (a) F
   (b) F
   (c) T
   (d) F
5. (a) 1.7×10^3 J
   (b) 5.0 kg
9. 0.39 m

5.1, pp. 67–68

1. F
2. bowling ball
3. (a) $0.48 \text{ k} \cdot \text{m/s}$ [E]
   (b) $4.8 \text{ k} \cdot \text{m/s}$ [E]
4. (a) T
   (b) T
5. momentum, impulse
6. (b) momentum
8. (a) $120 \text{ N} \cdot \text{s}$ [S]
   (b) $120 \text{ N} \cdot \text{s}$ [S]
9. 0.21 s
10. $19 \text{ N} \cdot \text{s}$ [W]

5.2, pp. 69–70

2. normal, equal
4. $m_1 \Delta \vec{v}_1 = -m_2 \Delta \vec{v}_2$
7. T
10. 2.50 m/s [W]

5.3, pp. 71–73

2. e.g., thermal, sound, potential
5. $\frac{1}{2} m_1 \vec{v}_{i_1}^2 + \frac{1}{2} m_2 \vec{v}_{i_2}^2$
   $= \frac{1}{2} m_1 \vec{v}_{f_1}^2 + \frac{1}{2} m_2 \vec{v}_{f_2}^2$
6. (a) elastic
   (b) inelastic
   (c) elastic
7. $\vec{v}_f = \dfrac{m_1 \vec{v}_{i_1} + m_2 \vec{v}_{i_2}}{m_2 + m_2}$

5.4, pp. 74–77

4. (a) F
   (b) T
7. 2.75 m/s [S]
8. 8.00 m/s [E]
11. mechanical, kinetic, elastic
12. (a) the spring constant
    (b) the compression of the object during the collision
13. $\frac{1}{2} m_1 \vec{v}_{i_1}^2 + \frac{1}{2} m_2 \vec{v}_{i_2}^2$
    $= \frac{1}{2}(m_1 + m_2)v_f^2 + \frac{1}{2}kx^2$
14. (a) cart 1: 40 m/s [left]; cart 2: 20 m/s [right]
    (b) 0.26 m

5.5, pp. 78–79

2. $\vec{p}_{i_{1x}} + \vec{p}_{i_{2x}} = \vec{p}_{f_{1x}} + \vec{p}_{f_{2x}}$
3. (c) 25 m/s
   (d) −34°

5.7, p. 81

1. the Sun, on Earth, electron, muon, tau, transform, Billions
2. (a) Wolfgang Pauli
   (b) neutron
   (c) Enrico Fermi

Chapter 5 Questions, pp. 83–84

1. (a) T
   (b) F
   (c) T
3. (a) $5.3 \text{ kg} \cdot \text{m/s}$ [forwards]
   (b) $3.6 \text{ kg} \cdot \text{m/s}$ [backwards]
   (c) $8.9 \text{ kg} \cdot \text{m/s}$ [forwards]
   (d) 1.0×10 m/s [forwards]
   (e) before: 92 J; after: 9.0×10 J; inelastic
4. yes
5. d
6. d

Unit 2 Questions, pp. 85–86

1. d
2. c
3. b
4. (a) F
   (b) F
   (c) T
5. 2.2×10^2 J
6. 3.5×10^2 kg
7. (a) 2.0×10 N/m
   (b) 24 J
8. 14 m/s
9. 110 s
10. 1.2 m/s at an angle of 29°

Unit 3

6.1, pp. 88–91

1. (a) T
   (b) T
   (c) F
   (d) T
3. (a) 1.6×10^7 m
   (b) 2.5×10^{-28} N
4. 26 cm
5. 3.5×10^{22} N
7. equal to
8. c
9. d
10. (a) 3.7 m/s^2
    (b) 2.6 times less

6.2, pp. 92–93

4. orbital radius
5. constant
6. (a) T
   (b) T
   (c) F
   (d) F
7. (a) 29.9 km/s
   (b) 2.00×10^{30} kg

Chapter 6 Questions, pp. 97–98

1. (a) iii
   (b) vii
   (c) i
   (d) ii
   (e) iv
   (f) v
   (g) vi
2. (a) F
   (b) T
3. 4.3×10^7 kg
4. (a) 16 times as great
   (b) no effect
5. 120 N

6. 3.3×10^{-1} N/kg
7. (a) 5.6×10^3 m/s
   (b) 16 days

7.1, pp. 99–100

1. b
2. 6.25×10^{18} electrons
3. 6.25×10^{12} electrons
4. b
5. a
6. c
7. T
8. d

7.2, pp. 101–102

1. a
2. d
3. 0.144 N
4. b
5. 21.8 N [N]

7.3, pp. 103–104

1. same, opposite
2. d
3. 9.73×10^6 N/C [N]
5. c
7. 3.8×10^7 N/C

7.4, pp. 105–106

1. a
2. -2.40×10^{-18} J
3. 1.42×10^3 N/C
4. c
5. b
6. 1.03×10^8 m/s
7. 2.59×10^6 J

7.5, pp. 107–108

1. d
2. 9.13×10^4 V
3. d
4. 2.30×10^{-18} J
5. 1.1×10^4 m/s
6. 2.82×10^{-14} m

7.6, pp. 109–110

2. b
3. -6.9×10^{-4} C.
4. 7.50×10^{14} electrons
5. 479 V
6. a
8. 5.15 μC

Chapter 7 Questions, pp. 112–113

1. c
2. b
3. (a) T
   (b) F
5. 5.54×10^6 N/C [NW]
6. 5.25×10^3 m/s
7. 15 elementary charges

8.1, pp. 114–115

1. b
2. a
3. (a) F
   (b) T
4. b
5. a
6. b
7. a
8. c

9. b
10. d

8.2, pp. 116–117

1. b
2. a
3. 1.44×10^{-12} N
5. a
7. 1.77×10^{-16} T

8.3, pp. 118–119

1. a
2. 1.01 N
4. a
5. 1.4 N
6. 0.0784 T [E]

8.4, pp. 120–121

1. c
2. 1.84 T
3. (a) 1.01
   (b) 0.0122 m or 12.2 mm
4. a
5. b

8.5, pp. 122–123

1. c
2. a
3. a
4. c
5. d
6. d
7. b
8. c
9. (a) T
   (b) F
   (c) T

8.6, p. 124

1. d
2. a
3. b
4. a
5. d
6. T

Chapter 8 Questions, pp. 126–127

1. a
2. b
3. (a) T
   (b) F
4. 9.35×10^{-18} N
5. 62.2 T
6. 6.80 cm

Unit 3 Questions, pp. 128–129

1. c
2. c
3. d
4. (a) F
   (b) T
   (c) T
5. 3.03×10^3 m/s
6. double the distance
7. 4.16×10^{-15} N

Unit 4

9.1, pp. 131–132
1. 3.0 m; 6.3 m; 0.25 s; 25 m/s
2. 0.122 m
3. 23.1 m/s
5. F
6. 196 m

9.2, pp. 133–134
1. medium 1
2. 12.5°
3. 2.17×10^8 m/s
4. b
5. 284 nm
6. c
7. d
8. 64.8°

9.3, pp. 135–136
1. a
2. Monday
3. 19°
5. 5.38 cm
6. 28.4 cm

9.4, pp. 137–138
1. d
2. a
5. a
6. F

9.5, pp. 139–140
1. c
2. d
3. F
4. c
5. T
6. 3.6×10^{-7} m
7. 521 nm
8. 0.221 mm

9.6, p. 141
1. a
2. d
3. T

Chapter 9 Questions, pp. 143–144
1. d
2. d
3. (a) T
   (b) F
4. 34.2°
5. 212 cm
6. 1.10×10^6 m
7. 14.9°
8. m_r: 2; m_v: 3

10.1, pp. 145–146
1. a
2. d
3. F
4. 400 nm
5. 9.10 μm
6. 450 nm

10.2, pp. 147–148
1. d
2. T
3. d
4. 0.0419 m
5. 1.80 m on either side of the central maximum
6. 536 nm
7. n_{blue}: 4; n_{red}: 3

10.3, pp. 149–150
1. c
2. b
3. (a) F
   (b) T
5. 489 nm
6. 63.2°
7. 476 nm

10.4, pp. 151–152
1. c
2. a
4. T
5. b
6. d
7. 3.00×10^4 m or 30.0 km
8. 1.14×10^{14} times

10.5, pp. 153–154
1. d
3. T
4. c
5. T
6. a
7. $\frac{3}{4}$
8. 75.8°

10.6, p. 155
1. d
2. b
3. d
4. (a) T
   (b) T

10.7, p. 156
1. a
2. a
3. b
4. (a) T
   (b) T

10.8, p. 157
1. d
2. b
3. c
5. T

Chapter 10 Questions, pp. 159–160
1. b
2. a
3. (a) F
   (b) T
4. 0.095 m
5. 31.3°
6. 3.89 times
7. 53.7°

Unit 4 Questions, pp. 161–162
1. a
2. d
3. (a) T
   (b) F
4. 1.51
5. 8.34°
6. 600 nm
7. 18.1°

Unit 5

11.1, pp. 164–165
1. d
2. c
3. 2.00 m/s [E]
4. d
5. b
6. c
7. b
8. T

11.2, pp. 166–167
1. d
2. 18 s
3. 60 min
4. 0.80c
6. F

11.3, pp. 168–169
1. c
2. 1.72 m
3. c
4. 2.3 times
5. 0.434c

11.4, pp. 170–171
1. T
2. 1.91×10^9 times
3. 0.990c
4. d
6. 0.999c

Chapter 11 Questions, pp. 173–174
1. c
2. b
3. (a) T
   (b) F
4. 2.76 s
5. 5.02×10^3 km
6. 0.866c
7. 3.60×10^{-28} kg

12.1, pp. 175–176
1. c
2. a
3. d
4. b
5. a
6. T

12.2, pp. 177–178
1. c
2. 1.36×10^{15} Hz
3. 3.85×10^{-24} J; 1.28×10^{-32} kg · m/s

4. energy, momentum, special relativity
5. c
6. T
7. 5.6×10^3 K

12.3, pp. 179–180
1. b
2. 2.87×10^{-15} m
3. 5.82×10^{-34} m
4. d
5. b
6. a
7. greater than 7.42×10^{-27} kg · m/s

12.4, p. 181
1. d
2. b
3. b
4. a
5. F

12.5, p. 182
1. b
2. a
3. b
4. encoding, decoding, passwords, Internet, secure
5. (a) F
   (b) F

12.6, pp. 183–184
1. b
2. d
3. c
5. a
6. c
7. a
9. d
10. b
11. c
12. F

Chapter 12 Questions, pp. 186–187
1. a
2. d
3. (a) T
   (b) F
4. 4.64 eV
5. 1.99×10^{-17} J; 6.63×10^{-26} kg · m/s
7. 6.44×10^{-15} m

Unit 5 Questions, pp. 188–189
1. b
2. d
3. (a) F
   (b) F
4. 0.866c
5. 6.06×10^{-11} kg
6. no
7. greater than 1.05×10^{-14} m

Appendix

A-1 Taking Notes: Identifying the Main Ideas

- *Identify and highlight the main ideas.* Main ideas are key concepts within a text. Text features such as headings, subheadings, boldfaced or italicized words, and graphic clues help to identify the main ideas in a text.
- *Identify and underline the details.* Details clarify or elaborate on the main ideas within a text.
- When you study for an exam, focus on the main ideas, not the details.

EXAMPLE

The Wave Theory of Light

In 1665, Francesco Grimaldi, who was the first to use the term **diffraction**, suggested that observable diffraction took place when light passed through a narrow slit, creating rays of coloured light, thus showing that light was wavelike in nature.

Also in 1665, Robert Hooke developed the wave theory of light. Christiaan Huygens, in his *Treatise on Light* (1678), further developed Hooke's theory that light behaved as a wave. Huygens formulated the **wave principle**, called Huygens' principle, which states that all points on a wave front can be thought of as new sources of spherical waves. He also claimed that light required an invisible medium in which to travel called the **ether**. Huygens' theory helped explain the concepts of reflection, refraction, and diffraction using wave concepts for light.

Description/Discussion of Strategies

Read the sample text above and note the text features. Remember that text features such as headings and boldfaced words signal key concepts. Notice that the above text has the heading "The Wave Theory of Light". The heading is a text feature that tells you the topic of the text. It gives you important information and is, therefore, a main idea. Highlight the heading. Now look at the boldfaced words in the text: **diffraction**, **wave principle**, and **ether**. Boldfaced words identify vocabulary terms. Here, the boldfaced words are embedded in the vocabulary definitions and tell you what the words mean. Highlight vocabulary definitions as they are main ideas, too. Finally, take a look at the opening sentences in both paragraphs of the above text. The opening sentences give you a quick overview of the information in the two paragraphs, and should also be highlighted as key concepts.

Now that you have identified the main ideas in the above text, try to find the details. Look for sentences that add to the main ideas you identified above. The sentence "He also claimed that light required an invisible medium in which to travel called the ether," is an addition to the concept, "light behaved as a wave". It is a detail, and should be underlined. Similarly, the last sentences in each paragraph are also details, since they provide more examples of why light behaves as a wave. Underline these sentences.

Read the following text and complete the activities below.

Types of Electric Charge

A **static charge** is an electric charge at rest. The charge that you acquire as you walk across a carpet is called a static charge because it stays on you until you touch a metal doorknob. When you touch the doorknob, the charge moves from you to the door. Although some objects may keep a static charge for some time, eventually the static charge is **discharged**, or lost, to other objects in the air. Static charges tend to last longer indoors on winter days when the heated air is very dry. The study of static electric charge is called **electrostatics**.

1. Highlight the main ideas in the text.
2. Underline the details in the text.

Now read the following text and answer the questions that follow.

Some materials, such as acetate and vinyl, are able to acquire electric charges that stay on them for some time. These materials are called insulators. An **insulator** is a substance in which the electrons are so tightly bound to the atoms making up the material that they are not free to move to a neighbouring atom. Plastic is a good insulator. It is used to coat wires and extension cords to protect us from electric shock.

Other materials, such as aluminum and copper, are called conductors. A **conductor** allows electrons to flow freely from one atom to another. Metals are good conductors. Some materials, such as carbon, silicon, and germanium, are semiconductors because they allow electrons to move although there is some resistance.

1. Which sentence from the text does *not* contain a main idea?
   (a) An insulator is a substance in which the electrons are so tightly bound to the atoms making up the material that they are not free to move to a neighbouring atom.
   (b) Plastic is a good insulator.
   (c) It is used to coat wires and extension cords to protect us from electric shock.
   (d) A conductor allows electrons to flow freely from one atom to another.
2. Explain the difference between a main idea and a detail.

A-1 Taking Notes: Reading Strategies

The skills and strategies that you use to help you read depend on the type of material you are reading. Reading a science book is different from reading a novel. When you are reading a science book, you are reading for information.

BEFORE READING

Skim the section you are going to read. Look at the illustrations, headings, and subheadings.
- *Preview.* What is this section about? How is it organized?
- *Make connections.* What do I already know about the topic? How is it connected to other topics I already know about?

- *Predict.* What information will I find in this section? Which parts provide the most information?
- *Set a purpose.* What questions do I have about the topic?

DURING READING

Pause and think as you read. Spend time on the photographs, illustrations, tables, and graphs, as well as on the words.

- *Check your understanding.* What are the main ideas in this section? How would I state them in my own words? What questions do I still have? Should I reread? Do I need to read more slowly, or can I read more quickly?
- *Determine the meanings of key science terms.* Can I figure out the meanings of terms from context clues in the words or illustrations? Do I understand the definitions in bold type? Is there something about the structure of a new term that will help me remember its meaning? Which terms should I look up in the glossary?
- *Make inferences.* What conclusions can I make from what I am reading? Can I make any conclusions by "reading between the lines"?
- *Visualize.* What mental pictures can I make to help me understand and remember what I am reading? Should I make a sketch?
- *Make connections.* How is the information in this section like information I already know?
- *Interpret visuals and graphics.* What additional information can I get from the photographs, illustrations, tables, or graphs?

AFTER READING

Many of the strategies you use during reading can also be used after reading. For example, your textbook provides summaries and questions at the ends of sections. These questions will help you check your understanding and make connections to information you have just read or to other parts in the textbook.

At the end of each chapter are summary questions and a vocabulary list, followed by a Chapter Self-Quiz and Chapter Review.

- *Locate needed information.* Where can I find the information I need to answer the questions? Under what heading might I find the information? What terms in bold type should I look for? What details do I need to include in my answers?
- *Synthesize.* How can I organize the information? What graphic organizer could I use? What headings or categories could I use?
- *React.* What are my opinions about this information? How does it, or might it, affect my life or my community? Do other students agree with my reactions? Why or why not?

- *Evaluate information.* What do I know now that I did not know before? Have any of my ideas changed because of what I have read? What questions do I still have?

A-1 Taking Notes: Graphic Organizers

Graphic organizers are diagrams that are used to organize and display ideas visually. Graphic organizers are especially useful in science and technology studies when you are trying to connect together different concepts, ideas, and data. Different organizers have different purposes. They can be used to

- show processes
- organize ideas and thinking
- compare and contrast
- show properties of characteristics
- review words and terms
- collaborate and share ideas

TO SHOW PROCESSES

Graphic organizers can show the stages in a process (**Figure 1**).

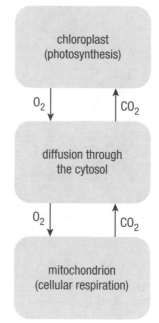

Figure 1 This graphic organizer shows that oxygen and carbon dioxide are transported throughout the plant cell.

TO ORGANIZE IDEAS AND THINKING

A **concept map** is a diagram showing the relationships between ideas (**Figure 2**, next page). Words or pictures representing ideas are connected by arrows and words or expressions that explain the connections. You can use a concept map to brainstorm what you already know, to map your thinking, or to summarize what you have learned.

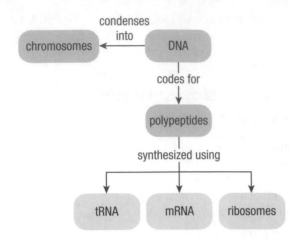

Figure 2 Concept maps show the relationships among ideas.

Mind maps are similar to concept maps, but they do not have explanations for the connections between ideas.

You can use a **tree diagram** to show concepts that can be broken down into smaller categories (**Figure 3**).

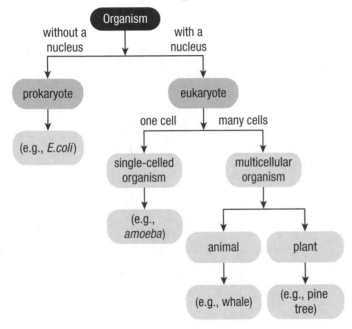

Figure 3 Tree diagrams are very useful for classification.

You can use a **fishbone diagram** to organize the important ideas under the major concepts of a topic that you are studying (**Figure 4**).

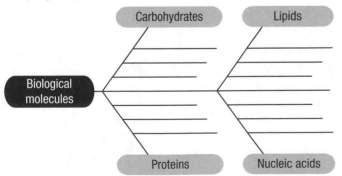

Figure 4 A fishbone diagram

You can use a **K-W-L** chart to write down what you know (K), what you want (W) to find out, and, afterwards, what you have learned (L) (**Figure 5**).

K	W	L
What I know	What I want to know	What I have learned

Figure 5 A K-W-L chart

TO COMPARE AND CONTRAST

You can use a **comparison matrix** (a type of table) to compare related concepts (**Table 1**).

Table 1 Subatomic Particles

	Proton	Neutron	Electron
electrical charge	positive	neutral	negative
symbol	p^+	n^0	e^-
location	nucleus	nucleus	orbit around the nucleus

You can use a **Venn diagram** to show similarities and differences (**Figure 6**).

Germ-cell mutations   **Somatic-cell mutations**

- changes reproductive cells
- can be passed to offspring

- modified DNA

- changes body cells
- not passed to offspring
- can lead to diversity and evolution

Figure 6 A Venn diagram

You can use a **compare-and-contrast chart** to show similarities and differences between two substances, actions, ideas, and so on (**Figure 7**).

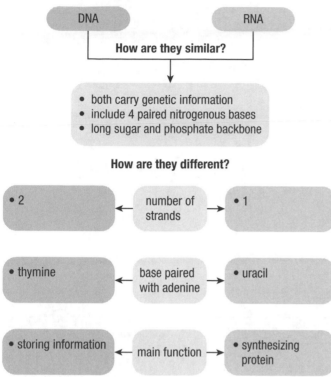

Figure 7 A compare-and-contrast chart

TO SHOW PROPERTIES OR CHARACTERISTICS

You can use a **bubble map** to show properties or characteristics (**Figure 8**).

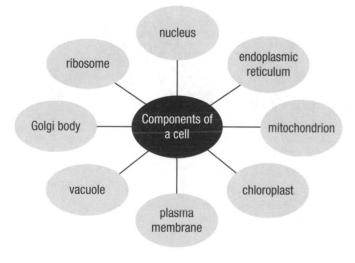

Figure 8 A bubble map

TO REVIEW WORDS AND TERMS

You use a **word wall** to list, in no particular order, the key words and concepts for a topic (**Figure 9**).

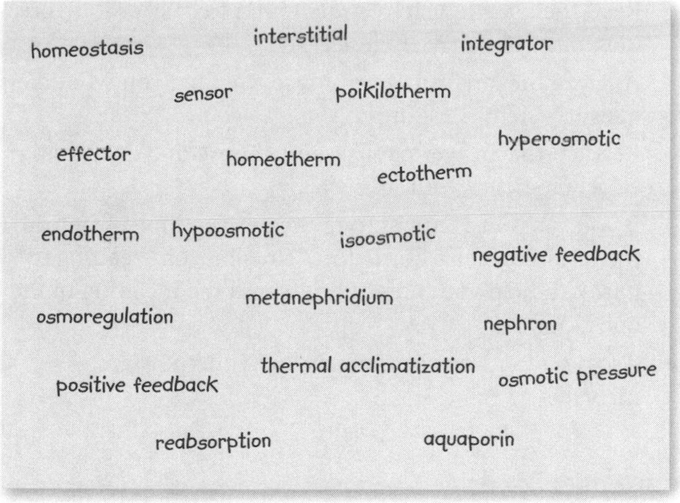

homeostasis   interstitial   integrator

sensor   poikilotherm

effector   homeotherm   hyperosmotic
ectotherm

endotherm   hypoosmotic   isoosmotic
negative feedback

metanephridium
osmoregulation   nephron

positive feedback   thermal acclimatization   osmotic pressure

reabsorption   aquaporin

Figure 9 A word wall

TO COLLABORATE AND SHARE IDEAS

When you are working in a small group, you can use a **placemat organizer** to write down what you know about a certain topic. Then all group members discuss their answers and write in the middle section what you have in common (**Figure 10**).

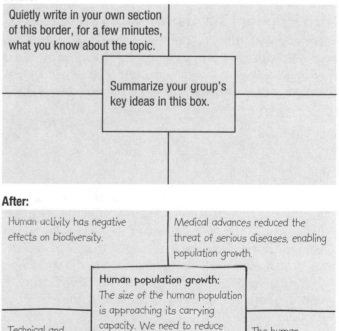

Figure 10 A placemat organizer

A-2 Answering Questions
A-2.1 Multiple-Choice Questions

- Read the question stem and attempt to answer it before looking at the answer choices.
- Analyze the key words or phrases that tell you what the question stem is asking.
- Read all the answer choices and choose one that most closely matches your answer.
- If your answer is not among the answer choices, reread the question stem. Sometimes slowing your reading pace can help you better understand the meaning of the question.
- Cross out any answer choices that you know are incorrect.

EXAMPLE

Read the following question stem:

A Canada goose flies at 40 km/h in still air. It is flying south on a day when a wind is blowing from the north at 25 km/h. What is the speed of the goose over the ground?

Description/Discussion of Strategies

Try to answer the question first without looking at the answer options (cover the options with a sheet of paper or with your hand). Then, look at the answer options below. Check your answer against the four choices given. Is your answer among the options? If yes, you have correctly answered the question.

(a) 0 km/h

(b) 15 km/h

(c) 40 km/h

(d) 65 km/h

If your answer does not match one of the options, use the next strategy. Underline the key words in the sample question. The key words and phrases are the essence of the question. They tell you what the question is expecting you to know or do. This sample question asks you to recognize that the speed of the goose is "40 km/h in still air". This would be its speed over the ground if there was no wind. However, there is a wind "blowing from the north at 25 km/h". Since the goose and wind are both moving south, the speed of the goose over the ground cannot be smaller than either 25 km/h or 40 km/h.

Look at the answer options. You can eliminate choices (a) and (b). You have narrowed your possible answers to (c) and (d). Since (c) is the speed of the goose in still air, and you know that there is a wind blowing, this cannot be the right answer. You are left with option (d), which is the correct answer.

Complete the following multiple-choice questions using the tips you have just read.

1. A skier is skiing downhill at a constant speed in a straight line. Which of the following statements is true?

   (a) There is no static friction between the skier and the snow.

   (b) There is no kinetic friction between the skier and the snow.

   (c) The normal force is equal to the component of the skier's weight parallel to the hill.

   (d) All of the above.

   Explain how you arrived at the answer to the above question.

2. Which of these is an example of a fictitious force in a non-inertial frame of reference?

   (a) The normal force acting on a bicycle going down a hill at constant speed in a straight line.

   (b) The gravitational force acting on a satellite in a circular orbit.

   (c) The force causing a hurricane to follow a curved path.

   (d) All of these are fictitious forces.

   Were there any key words or phrases within the stem that identify what the question is expecting you to know? Explain.

3. A commercial jet has taken off from a major airport and is climbing at a constant speed through the air. What happens to the work done by the engines during this climb?

   (a) The work becomes kinetic energy of a airliner.

   (b) The work becomes gravitational potential energy of the airline.

   (c) The work becomes heat energy due to friction with the air.

   (d) Both (b) and (c).

   Which answer choices were you able to eliminate and why?

A-2.2 Short-Answer Questions

A **short-answer question** is an open-ended question that requires a response. The question could ask for a definition, an explanation, or an example. It could also be a calculation or a completion activity. Depending on the type of short-answer question, the response will vary in length from a single sentence to a few sentences.

- Read the question carefully to understand the type of response required.
- Organize your response before writing it by making an outline, listing main points, drawing a sketch, or creating a graphic organizer.
- Make sure you answer all parts of the question. Eliminate any unnecessary information from your answer so it is clear and concise.

Read the following selection and answer the short-answer question:

Inelastic collisions are collisions in which some kinetic energy is lost. The kinetic energy is transformed into other forms, such as thermal energy or sound energy. Consider a collision involving a ball composed of soft putty or clay. The ball will not spring back at the end of the collision. Energy is absorbed, causing the kinetic energy after the collision to be less than the kinetic energy before the collision. The collision, therefore, is inelastic.

1. Describe what happens to kinetic energy in an inelastic collision, and why this happens.

Description/Discussion of Strategies

Read the question and identify what type of short-answer question it is. This sample question asks you to *describe* what happens to kinetic energy in an inelastic collision and why this happens. In other words, the question requires an answer that is at least a couple of sentences long. Notice that several lines have been provided for you to write your answer. Use this to estimate your answer's length. Start by writing down the main points that your answer should cover. These notes will help you craft a complete answer. The sample notes below list the main points regarding kinetic energy in an inelastic collision.

SAMPLE STUDENT NOTES:

– *kinetic energy is not conserved in an inelastic collision*

– *kinetic energy is transformed into other forms of energy, such as thermal energy or sound energy*

– *inelastic collisions usually involve non-elastic materials, such as soft putty or clay*

You will build your answer from these bullet points. After writing an answer, read it to make sure you have answered the question correctly and completely.

Finally, eliminate any information in your answer that is unnecessary or that does not pertain to the question. If your response is very long, condense the information to make it brief and succinct.

SAMPLE ANSWER:

Inelastic collisions usually involve non-elastic materials such as soft putty or clay. Kinetic energy is absorbed and transformed into other forms of energy such as thermal energy or sound energy. The total kinetic energy after the collision is less than the total kinetic energy before the collision.

Complete the following short-answer questions, using the selections below and the tips you just read.

Universal Gravitation

Newton's law of gravitation plays a key role in physics for two reasons. First, his work showed for the first time that the laws of physics apply to all objects. The same force that causes a leaf to fall from a tree also keeps planets in orbit around the Sun. This fact had a profound effect on how people viewed the universe. Second, the law provided us with an equation to calculate and understand the motions of a wide variety of celestial objects, including planets, moons, and comets.

1. Summarize two reasons why Newton's law of gravitation plays a key role in physics.

A-2.3 True/False Questions

Many true or false questions connect two ideas, or a person with an idea.

- Read the statement carefully.
- Identify the main ideas in the statement.
- Decide whether the ideas are connected or not.

EXAMPLE

Decide whether the following statement is true or false.

Einstein introduced the hypothesis that light energy comes in discrete packets called quanta in order to explain the photoelectric effect.

Description/Discussion of Strategies

Read the question carefully. This statement consists of a person and two ideas. Decide which concepts are connected.

- Is Einstein associated with the photoelectric effect? Did he apply the quantum theory to explain the effect?

If both answers are yes, the statement is true. If either is false, the statement is false. The statement above is TRUE.

PRACTICE

Is the following statement true or false? If the statement is false, rewrite it to make it true.

1. According the classical theory, an electron in a circular orbit in the Rutherford model of the atom should be stable.

What concepts did you identify in this statement?

A-2.4 Matching Questions

Matching questions typically present two lists. The task is to match items from the first list with items from the second list.

- Study the items on the first list, and ensure that you understand the common characteristic of all of the items.
- Study the items on the first list, and ensure that you understand the common characteristic of all of the items.

- Look for obvious matches that you can recognize immediately.
- Then, continue with less obvious matches. Even if there are some items that you are not familiar with or cannot remember, you can often reduce the choices available.

EXAMPLE

Match the physicist on the left with an associated principle or concept on the right.

(a)	Albert Einstein	(i)	matter waves
(b)	Isaac Newton	(ii)	the elementary charge
(c)	Robert Millikan	(iii)	electric force on a current-carrying wire
(d)	André Marie Ampère	(iv)	special theory of relativity
(e)	Louis de Broglie	(v)	universal gravitation

Description/Discussion of Strategies

Start by checking the common characteristics: all items on the first list are physicists, and all items on the second list are principles or concepts.

Next, look for an obvious match. Most people associate Einstein with relativity. Continue making matches. If there are two or more left that you do not know, you may need to make an educated guess.

PRACTICE

Match the physical quantity in the first list with the SI unit in the second list.

(a)	electric current	(i)	T
(b)	mass	(ii)	N
(c)	weight	(iii)	C
(d)	magnetic field strength	(iv)	kg
(e)	quantity of electric charge	(v)	A

A-2.5 Extended Response Questions

Extended-response questions take more thought and planning. The quality of your response determines how much of the allotted mark you will receive. You must prepare by being very familiar with all aspects of the subject that the question is based on.

Most extended responses include:

- An introductory paragraph that introduces your main idea or the point you intend to make in your answer. You can often restate the question as all or part of your introduction.

- A core section that provides information points, examples, and possibly simple sketches to support and flesh out the main idea from the introductory paragraph. Include all that you know about the topic that is relevant to the question being asked. Most questions are crafted such that one paragraph will suffice for this section, but you may need more paragraphs if there is more than one main idea.

- A final concluding paragraph that sums up your main idea. You can include a restatement of your main idea similar to the first paragraph. Try to phrase your sentences as definite, confident statements.

1. GPS technology is becoming increasingly ubiquitous in our everyday routines. Some cell phones now include a GPS receiver that can be used for various purposes. Give examples of potential good or harm of this technology in a cell phone.

Description/Discussion of Strategies

Decide on your main ideas. The number of marks allotted to a question is often a good clue as to how many points the tester is looking for. Jot down as many ideas as come to mind. You need not use all of them. List possible applications of cell phone GPS technology, and their potential for good or harm.

SAMPLE STUDENT IDEAS

- *injury: in a remote area such as a hiking trail, the cell phone can send your exact position to search and rescue personnel. Good: help will reach you sooner.*
- *advertising: your position near a particular business establishment can trigger a text urging you to make a purchase. Good: you may be advised of a sale on an item you want. Bad: your privacy is being invaded.*
- *crime: if your phone is stolen, it can be programmed to send its GPS coordinates when the number is dialed, giving the location of the thief. Good: your property is returned.*
- *a criminal can intercept position information from a motorist stranded in a remote location, and use the information to commit a crime. Bad: GPS makes the crime possible.*

Now, you can use your ideas to write the introductory paragraph.

SAMPLE INTRODUCTORY PARAGRAPH

Cell phones that are GPS-enabled can be used for good, such as locating a lost hiker. They can also be used for harm, such as locating an easy target for the commission of a crime.

Next, use your ideas to give examples of your main points. It is not necessary to use all of the ideas. Use the number of marks allotted and the space left for the answer to guide the length of your replay. In this case, it would be wise to include one example of a good use of the technology, and one example of its potential for harm.

SAMPLE CORE SECTION

A hiker lost on a remote hiking trail may also be injured, or under threat from violent weather or failing daylight. The GPS-enabled cell phone can inform rescue personnel of the hiker's position within a few metres. Instructions can be given to the hiker on how to return to civilization, or a rescue party can be dispatched to a known location for a quick resolution of the problem.

A criminal can use the location of a person with a GPS-enabled cell phone to commit a crime. For example, the driver of a broken-down car in a remote location may phone for help, sending the GPS coordinates. A criminal will be monitoring the cell phone frequencies for this kind of information, and may reach the stranded motorist before help does.

Finally, wrap up your answer with a concluding paragraph.

SAMPLE CONCLUSION

Like most technologies, a GPS-enabled cell phone can be used for good or harm. It is up to the user to make use of the advantages while taking precautions against possible criminal use.

Write an extended response for the following question, making use of the tips you have just read.

1. The Michelson-Morley experiment was pivotal in providing Einstein with important facts for his theory of special relativity. Explain what the purpose of the experiment was, and how the result of the experiment fit into special relativity.

In your response, circle one of the main ideas in your introductory paragraph. Then underline the evidence you provide for it in the core section of your response.

A-3 Solving Numerical Problems Using the GRASS Method

In physics, you sometimes have problems that involve quantities, units, and mathematical equations. The GRASS method is an effective method for solving these problems. This method always involves five steps: Given, Required, Analysis, Solution, and Statement.

SAMPLE PROBLEM

Two metal spheres are each given a charge of 400 μC. Their centres are separated by 12.6 cm. What is the electrical force between them?

Given: $q_1 = 4.00 \times 10^{-4}$ C;
$q_2 = 4.00 \times 10^{-4}$ C;
$r = 0.126$ m

> Read the problem carefully and list all the values that are given. Remember to include units, and convert to SI if needed.

Required: F_E

> Read the problem again and identify the value that the question is asking you to determine.

Analysis: $F_E = \dfrac{kq_1q_2}{r^2}$

> Read the problem again and think about the relationship between the given values and the required value. There may be a mathematical equation you could use to calculate the required value using the given values. If so, write the equation down in this step. Sometimes it helps to sketch a diagram of the problem.

Solution:

$$F_E = \frac{kq_1q_2}{r^2}$$

$$= \frac{(8.99 \times 10^9 \; N \cdot m^2/C^2)(4.00 \times 10^{-4} C)(4.00 \times 10^{-4} C)}{(0.126 \; m)^2}$$

$$F_E = 9.06 \times 10^4 \; N$$

> Use the equation you identified in the "Analysis" step to solve the problem. Usually, you substitute the given values into the equation and calculate the required value. Do not forget to include units and to round your answer to an appropriate number of significant digits. (See Skills Handbook Sections A5.2 and A5.6 in your textbook.

Statement: The electric force between the spheres is about 9.06×10^4 N.

> Write a sentence that describes your answer to the question that you identified in the "Required" step.

PRACTICE

Solve the following problems using the GRASS method.

1. A point charge of 6.40 µC is moving in the *xy*-plane with a speed of 51.3 m/s at an angle of 35.0° with the positive *x*-axis. A magnetic field of 4.38 T lies parallel to the positive *z*-axis. Determine the magnetic force acting on the charge.

2. A diamond with refractive index 2.42 is dropped into water with refractive index 1.33. What is the critical angle for a ray of light crossing the boundary from diamond into water?